D1598022

# Lotus 25

# COVENTRY CLIMAX FWMV

A TECHNICAL APPRAISAL

# Lotus 25

# COVENTRY CLIMAX FWMV

A TECHNICAL APPRAISAL

IAN BAMSEY

A **FOULIS** MOTORING BOOK

First published 1990



Published and printed in England by:
J. H. Haynes & Co. Ltd.
Sparkford, Near Yeovil, Somerset BA22 7JJ,
England

Haynes Publications Inc.
861 Lawrence Drive, Newbury Park,
California, 91320, USA

Produced for GT Foulis & Co. by .
**RACECAR ENGINEERING**
(Racecar Engineering Specialist Publications)
Editorial Director: Ian Bamsey
Research Assistant: Alan Lis

British Library Cataloguing in Publication
Data
Bamsey, Ian
Lotus 25 Climax FWMV - a technical
appraisal.
1. Racing cars
I. Title
629.228

ISBN 0-85429-802-9

Library of Congress Catalog
Card number 90-80308

Typesetting & Artwork by:
Photosetting, Yeovil, Somerset

# CONTENTS

# INTRODUCTION

The Lotus 24 and the Lotus 25 shared the same engine, the same transaxle and the same four 'corners': only the central fuselage differed. The Lotus 24 was a conventional early Sixties mid engine design in so far as it was based on a multi-tubular frame carrying aluminium fuel tanks and clothed in g.r.p. panels. It was one of the most advanced of its breed yet it was far from an ideal solution to the engineering problems posed by the 1.5 litre Formula One.

In essence, the 1961-imposed Formula demanded a light car with a small frontal area: no longer was there power to spare overcoming weight or aerodynamic drag. Further, an emerging breed of high grip racing tyre demanded a sophisticated suspension and in turn that called for a rigid chassis structure. It was not possible to obtain high rigidity from a conventional tubular frame while fuel accommodation was another major headache.

The small, light Type 24 boasted advanced suspension geometry but inherently lacked structural rigidity. Further, it radically reclined its driver to help achieve a low frontal area and ended up with a lot of fuel perched over his legs in the scuttle. Creator Colin Chapman felt there had to be a better way. The inspired Lotus chief found it in the radically different Type 25 which he introduced at Zandvoort in May 1962.

Chapman had noted that the Coventry Climax V8 engine designed specifically for the new formula was capable of accepting chassis loads and he incorporated it and its fuel tanks into his new-style fuselage. Although called a monocoque, this structure did not consist of an aircraft-style single shell. Instead, Chapman set two torsion boxes either side of the powertrain and the driver, these boxes wide and deep enough to form rigid flanks for the fuselage while providing the required fuel accommodation. Bulkheads and the engine tied the two boxes firmly together while the engine and driver squeezed between them, the narrow cockpit closed by a g.r.p. shroud.

The interlinked boxes formed the basis of a fuselage no wider than the heads of the semi-stressed V8 engine while the fuel was carried beneficially low. The driver no longer had to peer over a scuttle tank and he was reclined further than ever. Thus, the new structure allowed Chapman to build a car smaller than ever while achieving an unprecedented level of torsional rigidity. That allowed him to work his tyres better than his rivals. The Lotus monocoque was more efficient than a tubular frame as a chassis, and it made for a more effective car. On track the Lotus 25 was a major step forwards from the Type 24 which Chapman had introduced only a few months earlier.

Both models were propelled by the Coventry Climax V8, the intriguing development of which set a pattern for future racing engines. Walter Hassan's FWMV was the bridge between the first petrol fuelled Grand Prix engines that ran to only a four figure speed and a future generation that would comforta-

bly achieve five figures without significant loss of brake thermal efficiency, and firmly in retention of a broad power band. The Climax philosophy was to ensure good driveability above all and Hassan's evolving creation served the Lotus 25 extremely well.

Of course, the Climax-Lotus FWMV-25 will always be remembered as the car in which Jim Clark shot to fame. Clark wrung every last ounce of potential out of Chapman and Hassan's clever creations, and he made it look easy in the manner of all truly Great drivers. Right from its first race at Zandvoort, Clark-FWMV-25 was the quickest combination in Grand Prix racing and the Scot duly won the 1963 World Championship. This book studies his equipment while hopefully not overlooking the importance of his driving genius.


# Acknowledgments

This volume would not have been possible without the kind co-operation of key figures in the Lotus 25 story including Lotus' early Sixties Technical Director Mike Costin, and Dick Scammell who helped build the prototype chassis. Cedric Selzer was another member of the Lotus team in the 25 days and he has more recently restored the remains of chassis R5 to its former glory. He filled in many details while Jack Leonard of Dunlop provided tyre information.

The design and development of the Climax V8 engine has been well documented, in particular by Walter Hassan's autobiography 'Climax in Coventry' and by S.A.E. paper 660742, which he presented to the society in 1966.

Another valuable source of reference was the documentation of the period provided by contemporary specialist motoring journals, in particular *Motor Sport, Autosport* and *Motoring News*. Acknowledgement is also due to John Thompson's Formula One Record Book, published in 1974, and to L.J.K. Setright's History of the Grand Prix Car 1954-66, published in 1966. Both were long out of print at the time of writing.

The photographs are from the archives of London Art Tech (LAT), Standard House, Bonhill Street, London EC2A 4DA.

# BACKGROUND

# Defying Gravity

The period 1958 - 1961 witnessed the dramatic fall of the classic wire wheel Grand Prix car as typified by the Maserati 250F with which Fangio won the 1957 World Championship. Fangio sat bolt upright behind a bellowing engine that was burning a potent 'witches brew' including eye watering nitromethane. His plump, heavy machine had a spectacular excess of power over grip and he controlled dramatic slides with armfuls of opposite lock. Over the next four years new sporting and technical regulations slashed engine power while chassis and tyre advances dramatically improved grip.

The engine moved behind the cockpit and the Grand Prix car shrank in size. By 1961 its driver was lying almost flat in a pencil slim, lightweight fuselage with a diminutive engine sipping pump petrol inches from his shoulder blades. Engine power had fallen but the new age pilot found his car ultra responsive, its tyres offering an unprecedented level of adhesion. Consequently, he worked without sweeping gestures, careful not to waste power in slides, conducting through flick of the wrist.

For 1961 engine capacity had plummeted down from 2500cc. to 1500cc. and engines now had to run on 101.5 (RON) octane pump petrol rather than 130 octane Avgas, the new Formula One thereby contriving to keep power well below 200b.h.p. (at least for the time being). Nevertheless, in 1961 Phil Hill made the first sub-nine minute lap of the daunting 14 mile long Nurburgring.

Although unspectacular, the mid engine flyweight was certainly effective. It had found its genesis in the 1958 regulations which restricted fuel from exotic blends to Avgas and shortened races from a minimum of three hours to two hours. That trimmed engine power and opened up the possibility of non-stop races putting a premium on smaller, lighter and more economical designs. The freakish mid engined Cooper had grown up from revolutionary 500cc. motorcycle engine racer to crude, underpowered Grand Prix car and clearly profited from the new conditions.

John Cooper sparked the mid engine revolution almost by accident, his timely arrival in Formula One the culmination of steady progress through the Junior formulae. His unconventional machine benefited from less weight, better weight distribution and less frontal area than a traditional racing car. With its mid engine layout handling was enhanced since a lower moment of polar inertia made it more manoeuvrable, more responsive (though the front - rear weight distribution remained in the region of 40% - 60%). At the same time lower weight and lower frontal area (lessening aerodynamic drag, which is the product of frontal area and a non dimensional drag co-efficient) enhanced fuel consumption and provided more performance per b.h.p.

The chassis revolution of the late Fifties was complemented and reinforced by major strides in tyre development. The front engined cars of the Fifties had employed simple, almost crude chassis - early development of the 250F consisted of cutting tubes away in the cockpit area to relax the frame - and ran on somewhat primitive tyres. Pirelli ruled the roost (with the exception of the Daimler Benz days, which belonged to Continental) and Stirling Moss had to switch his private 250F from Dunlop to the Italian make to make it competitive. However, it was Dunlop that led the way into tyres that made gravity-defying cornering a reality before the advent of aerodynamic downforce.

Mid Fifties front engined cars were capable of generating a cornering force of the order of 0.75

g. The tubed crossply tyre that produced that measure as its co-efficient of friction had a cotton carcase and a natural rubber tread. Its domed crown carried a tread around three inches wide and its aspect ratio - the ratio of its section height (measured from bead level to the top of the crown) to section width (measured between bulging sidewalls) - was typically around 100%. This sort of tyre was manufactured by Dunlop in the guise of its R1 and R3 models, the former introduced in 1948, the latter in 1955.

Significantly, the R3 brought a carbon black rather than zinc oxide (white) based compound for carcase reinforcement. Whereas white casings had been limited to a maximum running temperature around 85 degrees, a black casing could tolerate up to 95 degrees. Subsequently all Dunlop's mid Fifties range - R1, R3 and R4 - contained carbon black. The R4 tyre was a wet weather version of the R3 (while R2 had been dropped at the development stage). An even more significant development came in 1958: the nylon ply carcase. Pioneering nylon R3 Formula One tyres were run by Vanwall that year and lap times fell in spite of the compulsory use of Avgas largely for that reason.

The new carcase offered greater flexibility with greater tensile strength. The flexibility allowed the tyre to conform to the road better, increasing the effective footprint area by as much as 10% while the strength allowed a thinner, cooler running casing with more even heat distribution. The net result was improved grip, while a potentially lower inflation pressure could (in theory) further enhance adhesion on bumpy surfaces. With the nylon carcase there was more room adjust inflation pressure in accordance with driver preference and car suspension requirements. With the cotton carcase a pressure in the region of 50p.s.i. had been called for - now significantly lower pressures could be safely run.

During 1958 Dunlop developed the lower profile R5 tyre based on a nylon carcase. For 1959 the R5 superseded the R1, the R3 and the R4 and it was made available in two pattern depths: Normal, with a 8mm. depth for long distance racing and "Speed" with a 5mm. depth. Taking advantage of the new carcase technology, the R5 had an aspect ratio in the region of 70% and, for Formula One a rear tread width in excess of four inches. It was a major step forward and the following year Dunlop phased in a so called D9 version of it which was lighter and had a higher grip compound. Weight was saved by eliminating the rubber layer between the carcase and the tube and by eliminating separate sidewall rubber. The unsprung weight advantage was of the order of 2lb. per corner and the extra grip was immediately evident in further improved lap times.

The advent of the 1.5 litre formula found all Grand Prix cars on Dunlop tyres and regularly running the D9 version of the R5, with the harder compound, cooler running D10 version on hand for abrasive circuits and the even harder D11 available for extreme conditions. Although it had a monopoly, Dunlop did not give up development - it continued to move the goalposts for any potential rival. During 1960 Moss had won a wet Formula Two race at the Nurburgring running a Dunlop radial from a Porsche road car. Concern at the potential danger of these tyres being raced on a drying track helped spur the development of an R5 tyre with improved wet weather performance.

The so called D12 version sported the first ever synthetic rubber tread to be used in Formula One. The synthetic compound was high hysteresis whereas natural rubber is low hysteresis, the term hysteresis referring to a material's capacity for energy absorption. Since the synthetic tread absorbed more energy it provided superior damping. Further, a high hysteresis tyre was known to work better in wet conditions. However, although synthetic rubber could tolerate higher temperatures - raising the threshold as high as 110 degrees - in the dry it had a tendency to develop dangerously high temperatures and to wear faster.

Nevertheless, synthetic rubber was now commonly used for production tyres. At the far lower performance and hence temperature levels experienced by road cars synthetic tyres were in no danger of going off let alone blistering, or of wearing unduly fast let alone chunking. However, racing was a different matter and thus Formula One cars had so far been running exclusively on natural rubber which was more reliable at very high performance levels.

The synthetic rubber tread of the new D12 was

based on Styrene Butadiene Rubber (SBR). The tyre worked extremely well in the wet - startling teams with its performance upon its baptism in an Aintree storm - and drivers soon found that it offered superior grip in the dry. It retained the familiar R5-type construction and tread pattern while the softer tread was evident from comparative durometer readings: 70 for the D10, 68 for the D9, 64 for the D12. These are readings of hardness taken when cold and hot the difference was even more pronounced since synthetic rubber softens more than natural rubber as temperature rises.

In general terms, softer rubber offers more grip but wears faster. Significantly, the D12 version of the R5 needed the cooling effect of a wet track. At the 'Ring in '61 Moss started his Rob Walker Lotus 18 on D12s on a damp track, against the advice of the Dunlop technicians who warned that the track wasn't wet enough to keep temperature and wear rate under control. Looking to match the more powerful Ferraris, Moss gambled on the fact that the Nurburgring produced the lowest tyre temperatures of all Grand Prix circuits and that by avoiding slides he could help keep his tyre temperature down. He built a significant lead as the track steadily dried, then drove gingerly and prayed for rain. His prayer was answered with a short shower and he took a famous victory on well worn rubber...

Dunlop introduced the famous green spot - a one inch disc on the sidewall - to immediately identify D12 versions of the R5 tyre and discouraged their use on a dry track. Thus, standard wear for 1961 1.5 litre Formula One cars was the D9 on a dry track (rarely was the D10 called for), the D12 on a wet track, both in "Speed" guise. Interestingly, drivers did not try qualifying on green spot tyres: everyone ran D9s unless conditions dictated otherwise. Had one team switched to D12s for qualifying the green spot would have made the ploy obvious, everyone else would have followed so the advantage would straight away have been lost. However, it was advantageous to start a dry race on partly worn tyres, these having worn to the ideal profile for the car and offering better tread stability.

The regular D9 tyre had the potential to produce a cornering force approaching 1.0 g. Given the cut in engine power implicit in the '61 regulations it was more important than ever to make the most of the potential of the available tyres, which were clearly far more sophisticated than those employed in the days of the front engined sliders. And they were the same for everyone.

The key factors influencing the co-efficient of friction produced by any given tyre, aside from its inflation pressure and running temperature (and given no aerodynamic downforce) are car weight and suspension characteristics. The car should be a light as possible since as unit pressure rises anywhere in the rubber contact patch, the rubber is less able to resist frictional shearing forces. The height of the centre of gravity and weight transfer must also be taken into account and the latter is influenced by the suspension. Of course, the overall suspension performance is the most important chassis factor.

The early Sixties chassis designer had to play close attention to chassis roll and wheel control. Two major considerations were ride and camber. Soft springing was required to keep the tyre in contact with the road at all times - otherwise the tyre loading abruptly changed as the car hit bumps and that reduced the mean cornering force. At the same time Dunlop wanted tight control of camber. The ideal was to corner with the tyre vertical but under no circumstances in positive camber which robs cornering power.

To attain the right corner performance a little negative camber was run static, the amount lessening as the car rolled. If the chassis engineering was correct the amount of static negative camber was no greater than 1.5 degrees but as much as 2.5 degrees could be seen on some cars in 1961. More camber saw the car leaning more heavily on 'camber force' rather than pure 'cornering force' in a corner, while the inner edge of the tread would inevitably run hotter, particularly when most heavily loaded by the camber - when running in a straight line. Ferrari had exactly that problem on its World Championship winning machine.

The ideal car kept its tyres almost upright on the straight and no worse than upright when cornering. This car had the right roll centre location, dynamic weight distribution, roll stiffness and spring rate. Given those sometimes conflicting requirements, it was clear that a highly scientific approach was called for from the chassis designer. He had to pay careful attention to suspension geometry and, exploiting the obvious benefits of the new mid engine layout, had to devise a well planned chassis structure that was capable of handling the demands of the suspension.

It goes without saying that with less power and weight and given this level of sophistication the classic de Dion rear axle was no longer appropriate, nor was the leaf spring. Proper wheel control could only be achieved by fully adjustable, fully independent suspension front and rear. In the mid Fifties Cooper had introduced the concept of adjustable suspension but its suspension had been somewhat crude, retaining the old fashioned leaf spring. Contemporary Elva and Lola sportscars pioneered proper independent suspension with unequal length and non-parallel wishbones as the linkages and light, compact coils as the springing medium, these springs neatly and conveniently fitting over oil filled telescopic dampers.

The use of unequal and non-parallel wishbones provided tremendous scope for the designer: it allowed him to do almost anything with the wheel, albeit forcing him to compromise between many conflicting choices. Typically, in the case of British cars further compromise was enforced by the use of Triumph Herald uprights. Thus, although the most satisfactory form of linkage had been established by 1961 there was still a lot of scope for highly significant detail design. Further, chassis rigidity varied widely between makes.

A rigid chassis was required to successfully run soft springs. Indeed, rigidity was a crucial consideration since it only took a fractional relative movement of suspension pick up points to make a mockery of planned wheel control. Appropriately, the whippey ladder frame had given way to multi tubular construction. However, Cooper's 1959 and '60 World Championship winning interpretation was notorious with suspension pick ups hanging out on unsupported tubes and chassis rails curved to match body panels.

Cooper had also failed to make its double title winning car as light and as aerodynamically efficient as possible. Those factors were others that had become particularly significant in view of the '61 cut in engine power. Although the harnessing of aerodynamic downforce was still just a twinkle in Michael May's eye, reducing drag was now generally recognised as effective as extracting additional engine power, not just a special consideration for Monza and Rheims.

Since in 1961 all Grand Prix cars had the same tyres and had similar brakes - solid discs and two piston calipers supplied by Dunlop or Girling - aside from engine performance, the vital factors influencing lap times were all in the hands of the chassis builder. Colin Chapman was one of the few who fully appreciated the importance of chassis layout and rigidity, suspension design, overall weight and aerodynamic efficiency. That much was clear from his '61 Formula One design, but he had been slow to adopt the mid engine layout. An excellent engineer, Chapman could be a great innovator. Always he understood fully the nature of the challenge and sometimes he found a truly inspired answer to it.

Chapman had been Vanwall's chassis consultant and his first, late Fifties Grand Prix Lotus was a scaled down Vanwall, retaining the distinctive lines of the Frank Costin designed body shape with its claimed low drag co-efficient. Where Cooper put the four cylinder Climax behind the driver, Chapman canted it over Indy Roadster-style. Chapman's slimmed-down Vanwall shape presented a significantly smaller frontal area than the parent car but the Climax engine did not work well on its side. Ultimately it was that which forced Chapman to swallow his pride and follow Cooper's lead, embracing the greater potential of the mid engine layout.

Having gone the mid engine route Chapman made a proper job of it. He built his cars light (via an empirical process that on occasion threw up a disturbing structural failure) while ensuring chassis rigidity through proper attention to triangulation of the tubular framework. He fitted fully independent suspension at both ends of the car - with more precise geometry than most - and kept the frontal area low.

Chapman gradually shook off the Frank Costin influence, seeking to reduce frontal area rather than to massage the drag co-efficient. The Vanwall had been bulky but aerodynamic: Chapman's mid engine Lotus 18 of 1960 was as streamlined as a brick but was very small. The following year's Type 21 had more elegant lines but this was more aesthetics than scientific streamlining. Only trained aerodynamicist Carlo Chiti, working alongside racing car wing inventor Michael May down at Maranello paid any attention to wind tunnel testing at this stage in the development of the mid engine Grand Prix car.

Significantly, the Lotus 21 presented the lowest frontal area of all 1961 Grand Prix cars. Chapman instinctively knew that this brought him more benefit than any amount of scientific streamlining. The key to it was in reclining the driver to a degree previously undreamt of. Compared to the superseded 18, the 21 boasted a two inch lower driving position. From 18 to 21 the frontal area fell by almost a quarter of a square foot, a drop reckoned to represent around five horsepower gain through aerodynamic drag reduction.

During the mid Fifties Mercedes and others had gone the even further the other way than Costin producing low drag streamliners sporting full width bodywork. Tyre rotation can add a significant amount to total drag but under the '61 regulations it had become illegal to hide the wheels. The bodywork was not to cover the wheels in any plane, even at full lock. The cigar shape of the Lotus 21 was the logical form for the open wheel mid engine car's fuselage and its low frontal area put it a step ahead of its rivals in the quest for low drag.

On most counts the Lotus 21 was the state of the art in 1961, and it was the only car to get down to the 450kg. minimum weight limit. It had the lowest, slimmest fuselage ever seen, and a well engineered multi-tubular frame. The frame was designed to be as rigid as was possible given that the need for rapid driver entry and exit ruled out a pure 'spaceframe'. Compared to the Lotus 18, the Lotus 21 had improved rear suspension with the driveshafts relieved of the lateral loading imposed by doubling in the role of upper wishbones. Chapman sought to work his D9s to their full potential.

At the front end the upper wishbones were designed to act as rockers, operating inboard coils. Frontal area was reduced marginally, though not as much as it would have been had the rear springs also been hidden inboard and that was not very practical. The gain Chapman sought was reduced unsprung weight, assisting the operation of the suspension. Properly fabricated, the front rocker was more rigid than a conventional wishbone, necessarily so since it was subjected to high bending loads. The inboard front spring/damper unit's location was structurally sound since it relieved the less substantial lower wishbone of bending loads. It also kept the coil at the preferred angle for attack - a right angle - and allowed a shorter and attenuated anti roll bar.

With its ultra-slim fuselage, at Zandvoort the Lotus 21 proved faster in a straight line than Chiti's 20% more powerful '61 Ferrari in which the driver sat upright in conventional fashion. Indeed, right around the Dutch circuit Jim Clark's low slung, high grip, lightweight chassis allowed him to challenge the Italian cars in spite of the 30b.h.p. power deficit. Nevertheless, Ferrari dominated the '61 season on sheer horsepower. Ferrari had been in the position of having the only multi-cylinder engine ready for the new formula. Engine development had slowed somewhat since the mid Fifties due mainly to a lack of resources.

The days of Great Marques battling for supremacy had given way to a struggle between small teams of limited means, the majority relying on outside suppliers for parts such as brakes, suspension components and in particular the engine. Not only Cooper and Lotus but most other teams aside from the old established Ferrari and BRM stables looked to Coventry Climax, the fire pump manufacturer, for motivation.

For political as well as financial reasons both Coventry Climax and BRM had failed to respond quickly to the requirements of 1961. The stopgap 1.5 litre Formula Two version of the four cylinder Climax FPF engine run by all the British teams - even BRM - in 1961 only ran to 7,500r.p.m. whereas the Ferrari V6 screamed to a five figure speed. The higher revolutions allowed it to handle more air. More fuel can be poured into an engine almost at will but to produce more power there must be a corresponding increase of oxygen to burn with it. That simple truth was the basis of the 30b.h.p. advantage for the World Championship win-

*At last Ferrari faced some real challenge in the 1.5 litre Formula power stakes. This 90 degree V8 from Coventry Climax arrived at the Nurburgring in '61, slashing the Maranello horsepower advantage. Note the complex tuned exhaust system linking pipes from opposite banks.*

ning multi-cylinder Ferrari.

The V6 Ferrari was an uprate of a Formula Two engine penned in 1956 by Vittorio Jano (father of the innovative Alfa Romeo P3 and Lancia D50 Grand Prix cars) assisted by Ferrari's son Dino. Tragically Dino died before the engine raced and the model took his name. Designed for front mounted application, it had a 65 degree angle between banks and crank pins phased at 55 and 185 degrees. 55 degrees plus the 65 degrees afforded by the engine's architecture is 120 degrees, as is 185 degrees less 65 degrees. The five-bearing engine was run as three vee twins, each firing its cylinders in turn. Each cylinder fired at 120 degrees after the preceding impulse: six times 120 degrees is, of course, 720 degrees - one complete four stroke cycle.

First seen in a combined Formula One and Two race at Naples in 1957, the 1500cc. Dino engine (70 x 64.5mm.) had been specifically designed to run on pump petrol. It had twin overhead camshafts and two valves per cylinder opened by mushroom tappets screwed to the stem and closed by coil rather than Maranello's regular hairpin springs. The Ferrari valves were set at an included angle of 60 degrees, Jano specifying a typical hemispherical head and domed piston crown.

The valve disposition produced a compact chamber while the 65 degree vee angle allowed Jano to provide good downdraught induction passages. Weber as usual supplied special twin choke carburettors while twin plug ignition helped ensure good combustion. On a 9.5:1 compression ratio and running to 9,000r.p.m. the light alloy engine produced a commendable 180b.h.p. Chiti modified the chain driven unit for 1961, increasing the bore (going to 72 x 58.8mm.) for a larger piston area - 39 square inches in total - and a higher speed potential.

Seeking further improvement, Chiti devised a 120 degree version (which could not have fitted a front engined car) for better rotational balance, smoothing the quest to exceed 10,000r.p.m. This appeared early in the season and was available in two versions, offering 38.5mm. or 42mm. inlet valves (both having a 34mm. exhaust). The small valve version was tuned to produce its peak torque at 7,200 rather than 8,700r.p.m. It gave 170b.h.p. running to 9,000r.p.m. whereas the big valve version was coaxed to run to 10,500r.p.m. and offered a claimed 190b.h.p. at 10,000r.p.m. with strong top end power at the expense of a wide spread of power.

These power levels were particularly impressive when one considers that the 2.5 litre engines of the late Fifties had been hard pressed to exceed 100b.h.p. per litre on 130 octane Avgas. On Avgas the Vanwall engine produced 110b.h.p. per litre running to 7,500r.p.m, which represents 14.66b.h.p. per litre per 1000r.p.m. The Climax FPF produced a similar output per 1000 revolutions on Avgas, though no more than 250b.h.p. in total. Thus it offered only 100b.h.p. per litre, its peak power speed lower. The Ferrari V6's 'high' output of 127b.h.p. per litre at 10,000r.p.m. represented only 12.66b.h.p. per litre per 1000r.p.m. Clearly, it was purely higher engine speed that was responsible for the increase in power per litre of the 1961 Ferrari V6 over its 2.5 litre predecessors.

In general, spiralling frictional losses and pumping losses only marginally offset the power potential implicit in higher engine speed. Since the whole point of running to a higher speed is to handle a large volume of air and with it fuel to produce the additional power a real drawback is increased fuel consumption and hence a heavier fuel load. It is necessary also to consider the question of driveability.

Engine power is the product of torque - the turning force produced on the crankshaft by the combustion pressure acting on the pistons - and engine speed. High speed can compensate for poor torque in the search for peak power but for road racing the overall power characteristics must be taken into account. Hence the development of two versions of the 120 degree Ferrari V6. In general terms, road racing cars require useful acceleration over a wide range of engine speed. This implies a low rate of power fall off below peak power speed - in other words, a large area under the power curve.

Alas, as peak power speed is increased the curve of useful power tends to become straighter and steeper, and to cover a narrower r.p.m. band. The main reason is that volumetric (breathing) efficiency tends to fall off as speed increases. This, of course, was the problem Ferrari faced. At a lower operating speed there is a longer time interval between succeeding impulses in which aspiration can take place. Higher speed demands ever larger ports and valves to maintain volumetric efficiency. Larger valves do not tend to flow as well as smaller ones while in general larger bore ports cannot accelerate the airflow at lower engine speeds well enough to produce the turbulence necessary for good combustion.

It is possible to flow more air through an engine yet get less power. While breathing is important, volumetric efficiency must be matched by combustion efficiency. Combustion efficiency depends upon the design of the combustion chamber and upon there being the right degree of turbulence present during combustion. Turbulence affects the rate of burning and thus of pressure rise in the cylinder and is influenced by the compactness of chamber and by the porting. For a wide spread of power the porting will necessarily be a compromise. Ports must be large enough to allow the engine to breathe at top speed yet small enough to offer sufficient airspeed at lower r.p.m.

Thus, the challenge of the new formula for Ferrari and key rivals Coventry Climax and BRM was to maintain volumetric and combustion efficiency while increasing peak power engine speed. In view of this the latter half of '61 had found Climax and BRM somewhat belatedly working on V8 engines.

The d.o.h.c. V8s from Britain both entered the fray late in the '61 season, too late to upset the Ferrari domination. Both sported two valve, single plug 'hemi' heads, Climax with a 60 degree, BRM with an 80 degree included valve angle. Direct operation of coil spring closed valves through inverted bucket tappets was the order of the day. Whereas the Climax was gear and chain driven the BRM was fully gear driven. Both aluminium alloy engines carried iron liners and had four pin cranks running in five bearings and driven by conventional reciprocating gear.

Compared to a V6, the V8 configuration potentially provided more piston area: BRM boasted 45 square inches, having bore and stroke dimensions of 68.5 x 50.8mm. A smaller cylinder meant, theoretically, less stress for a given level of revolutions. However, it did not guarantee high volumetric efficiency nor good combustion. Nevertheless, the smaller cylinder of the V8 did lend itself to a good compact design of combustion chamber. Further, the fact that each cylinder was smaller offered the potential to run to a higher maximum speed.

All other things being equal, a smaller cylinder will produce less stress for a given engine speed. The increase in stress with rising engine speed is somewhat alarming and consideration of stress had traditionally limited engine speed to four figures. However, there is no specific 'stress barrier' and so long as an engine can last a race distance is can be considered to enjoy an acceptable level of stress, even if it has a tendency to fall apart on the slowing down lap. If it is good enough to win it is worth the effort of rebuilding for each subsequent race! The point is that in reality, the determination of acceptable levels of stress is a purely empirical process.

There are three main forms of stress in question: the stress produced by combustion pressure acting on the area of the piston, the stress produced by the inertia of the piston assembly as it is constrained to change direction at the ends of its stroke and a similar inertia stress set up in the valve train.

The stress loading felt by the piston is transferred to the crankshaft through the big end and is reacted to by the crankcase structure through the main bearings. There is also a centrifugal component involved due to the mass of the con rod and the main effect of this is to produce bending stresses in the rod itself. The most potentially destructive load is the inertia stress at top dead centre, which puts the con rod in tension. This is to some extent counteracted by combustion pressure but the effect of that decreases with speed since the inertia loads increase as the square of rotational speed.

Inertia loading can be expected to far exceed those stresses set up by combustion pressure on the piston. Further, the fact that inertia loading increases as the square of rotational speed means that the step from 9,000 to 9,500r.p.m., while a 5.5% increase in speed represents roughly a 10% increase in stress loading as felt by the engine.

The level of stress is proportional to piston acceleration and is a product of piston acceleration and the given inertia mass. That mass is clearly related to the size of the cylinder while piston acceleration is affected primarily by the length of the stroke, though con rod length plays a part. For a given speed, a longer rod reduces piston acceleration while a longer stroke significantly increases it.

So it is that the concept of a significantly over square 'short stroke' engine tends to be associated with high r.p.m. Further, overhead camshaft engines tend to be associated with high speed since pushrod assemblies cause significant inertia which has to be overcome before the additional load of opening the valve can commence. Valve train inertia is one problem of high speed, valve spring surge is another and even if the valve train can survive the inertia loading spring surge can make it impossible for a valve to follow its cam.

As we have seen, higher speed demands larger valves and it is a fact of life that larger valves don't like being opened and closed as quickly while their springs become more prone to surge. Thus larger valves are more difficult to control, presenting yet another challenge as engine speed rises. In the light of that Ferrari was considering a four valve per cylinder head, seeking smaller, lighter more controllable valves.

Coventry Climax was not yet seeking five figure speed. The new Climax V8 retained the 0.95 stroke:bore ratio of the FPF with dimensions of 63.0 x 60.0mm. for a 38 sq.in. piston area whereas the shorter stroke BRM had the stroke:bore ratio of 0.75 and a 19% greater piston area. The BRM had been designed from the outset for a five figure speed while the Climax V8 produced its peak power at 8,500r.p.m, at which speed, given its smaller cylinder it was far less stressed than the FPF. In this initial phase of development, Climax was concentrating upon a good spread of power. Thus, to promote high gas velocity the new V8 had relatively small ports and valves, which for its bore size were quite adequate. The Climax V8 had a 1.300in. (33.0mm.) inlet valve whereas the BRM V8 had a 1.562in. (39.7mm.) inlet valve. Further, Climax' small bore helped ensure a good combustion chamber shape (the narower valve angle was significant here) while its long stroke offset smaller piston area in translating combustion pressure into useful torque at the flywheel.

The so called FWMV was characterised by a 'viper's pit' exhaust system which interlinked pipes from cylinders on opposing banks, this telling of Climax' attention to pressure wave exhaust tuning principles to assist scavenging. BRM, on the other hand, carried distinctive individual cylinder exhaust 'stack pipes' in the interest of top end performance. At the speed it was running its primaries could not be made long enough to allow cross-bank interlinking. It was also noticeable that the BRM had the shorter inlet trumpets: Climax tuned both inlet and exhaust systems for a broad spread of power.

BRM took as its starting point high speed while Climax started out with its traditional emphasis upon driveability - high speed could follow. Interestingly, over the winter of '61/62 both Climax and BRM announced a peak power in the region of 180 - 185b.h.p. For a speed of 10,000r.p.m. that reflected badly on BRM while for a speed of 8,500r.p.m. the Climax output was encouraging. Climax was attaining 14.1b.h.p. per litre per 1000r.p.m., BRM only 11.4.

This winter Climax recorded a peak b.m.e.p. of 195.5p.s.i., BRM of 185p.s.i. With that the Coventry firm had a maximum torque of 118lb.ft. at 7,500r.p.m., BRM of 100.5lb.ft. at 9,000r.p.m. At 7,000r.p.m. Climax had 155b.h.p., BRM only 115b.h.p. At 8,000r.p.m. Climax had 175b.h.p., BRM 154b.h.p. Climax ran only to 8,500r.p.m., for a maximum of 181b.h.p. BRM ran on up to 10,500r.p.m. attaining 172b.h.p. at 9,000r.p.m., its peak of 184b.h.p. at 10,000r.p.m. with 181b.h.p. at maximum speed.

Climax' power band extended over one third of a much smaller speed range than BRM encountered. The BRM engine had to be wound up far more for a comparable output. Clearly BRM had not yet found a way to keep volumetric and combustion efficiency up with rising speed. However, it was early days yet and BRM had its eye on 12,000r.p.m. At that speed stress would not necessarily be much greater than experienced by a larger cylinder, longer stroke 2.5 litre four a few years earlier, in spite of the rate of piston acceleration involved.

During the 2.5 litre era a major curb on engine speed had been the traditional magneto ignition system which was hard pressed to supply more than 400 sparks per second - the requirement of an eight cylinder engine at only 6,000r.p.m. The Maserati V12 engine of 1957 turned to coil ignition and employed no less than 24 coils, one per plug. Coil ignition requires a steady battery voltage and this could later be ensured thanks to the development by Lucas of an effective racing alternator. That was available by 1961 while the then compulsory on board starter demanded an on board battery. Nevertheless, the mechanical contact breaker was a major drawback of coil ignition as it had been of magneto ignition.

Mechanically it was difficult to manufacture a cam, contact breaker heal and spring mechanism that would provide and maintain the required timing accuracy while electrically the points were a limiting item. Happily, by 1961 Lucas had developed a transistorised ignition system that could produce over 1000 high quality, properly timed sparks per second. The Lucas solid state ignition system cleverly eliminated the contact breaker and most other moving parts. Fed by an alternator charged battery, the new Lucas system could produce 1000 sparks per second without a drop in voltage and thus was capable of running an eight cylinder engine up to 15,000r.p.m.

Lucas was meanwhile in the process of developing of an eight cylinder fuel injection system, at first in conjunction with the Bourne engine. Crude injection systems had been common in the mid Fifties, alcohol fuel relatively insensitive to mixture strength. The switch to Avgas had seen a general reversion to Weber twin choke carburettors for greater precision in metering. Ferrari's close relationship with Weber was one factor that led BRM to investigate the sort of sophisticated injection system required for petrol. More importantly, effective fuel injection promised improved mixture distribution while allowing improved porting without the restriction of the carburettor venturi throat.

Lucas' innovative answer was an indirect system based on a 'shuttle-type' metering unit which was supplied fuel at a constant pressure via an electric pump. Throttle movement worked a cam which in turn controlled how far the shuttle at the heart of the metering unit could move. The shuttle was a free floating piston and varying the distance it could move determined precisely the amount of fuel fed to each cylinder's injector. The cylinder in which the shuttle operated rotated at engine speed uncovering ports through

*Walter Hassan (left, in white jacket) looks on as Jack Brabham debuts his Climax FWMV at the German Grand Prix meeting in August '61. Here the Cooper driver prepares for another lap of the 14 mile circuit, at last having performance worthy of the car carrying number one.*

which the measured and thus timed spurt of fuel was sent to each injector. Injection was into the inlet tract or trumpet rather than direct into the cylinder.

Meanwhile, down at Maranello Michael May was working on direct injection and Ferrari was contemplating the possibility of its own eight, possibly even twelve cylinder engine in the quest for ever higher speed. Fuel injection and high speed was indicative of the trend of Formula One engine development.

Porsche, the only other serious player under the new Formula One engine regulations, had an air cooled flat eight engine on the stocks to replace its existing four cylinder boxer. Alas, retention of the marque's traditional boxer configuration was a self inflicted handicap, due to excessive power loss to windage. In terms of the engine game, realistically it was a question of Coventry Climax and BRM threatening the early advantage of Ferrari, though with only 1.5 litres to play with the power game was no longer necessarily any more significant than the chassis contest.

Aside from the development of six speed gearboxes, however, the key chassis moves appeared to have all been made. Ferrari, Cooper (Jack Knight), Colotti and Porsche were toying with six speeds to match multi cylinder engine revolutions and power bands. Otherwise, with the highly refined Lotus 21 Chapman looked to have taken the new breed of lightweight mid engined machine to its logical conclusion. The main challenge appeared to be achieving 450kg. with the weight of a V8 engine (and the extra tankage it required) on board - the prototype V8 Cooper had weighed in at 530kg. Realistically, 1962 could be expected to offer close competition between 21-type cars on identical tyres with further engine developments the centre of technical interest. Chapman, however, had not yet finished exploring the frontiers of chassis technology...

## Formula One Regulations from 1961

Early Sixties FIA Formula One World Championship races were to run to a minimum of 300 kilometres or two hours and catered for 1500cc. cars with a minimum weight of 450kg. In addition to the World Championship for Drivers the qualifying events counted towards a Formula One Manufacturers' Cup, with a manufacturer's best place car only scoring points. Points were awarded on a 9-6-4-3-2-1 basis with only the best six scores to count. Where a chassis manufacturer employed an engine from another manufacturer the car was considered a 'Hybrid'. Where a Hybrid car won the Cup it was awarded to the chassis manufacturer. The World Championship was administered by the CSI on behalf of the FIA.

Cars were to run on 101.5 RON octane pump petrol ('commercial fuel as specified by the FIA') and supercharging was banned. The minimum weight of 450kg. was without fuel but with lubricant and coolant while any ballast had to be securely fixed to the chassis. The replenishing of lubricant during a race was forbidden and an oil catch tank to avoid spillage onto the circuit was mandatory. Another new requirement was a compulsory on board starter capable of being operated by the driver when seated in the car and with its source of energy on board. No more push starts away from the pits!

Fully enclosed bodywork was ruled out by a regulation demanding that all wheels be exterior to the body. Further, it was necessary for the driver to be able to occupy or abandon his seat without it being necessary to open a door or remove a body panel. A roll-over protection bar exceeding the height of the driver's head and the width of his shoulders was mandatory, as was regular safety equipment including a general electrical circuit breaker, but not seat belts. A dual braking system - in practice separate front and rear brake systems run from the same pedal - was also called for.

*The 1.5 litre Formula One brought new V8 engines from Coventry Climax and BRM. This is the Weber-equipped Climax FWMV as used by Lotus.*

62

# A Step too Far?

So often racing engine development has to be compromised in an effort to satisfy the logistics of racing programmes. Coventry Climax was in a particularly difficult position over the winter of '61/'62, having a lot of work to do on the late arriving FWMV V8 and having a lot of customers banging on the door. For some, four cylinder FPF engines would have to suffice until well into the new season. To the end of '61 only two FWMV engines had been built and these would be retained for Gray Ross' development department. For 1962 Harry Spear's production build and service department had orders for no less than 16 engines, four two car teams each taking three of the so called 'Mark II' '62 specification units. Clearly, a two car team suffering more than one engine failure in practice would have to resort to cannibalising to make the race. Climax had a reputation for reliable race engines and Technical Director Walter Hassan attended most Grand Prix meetings. He was assisted by Peter Windsor-Smith.

Climax' policy was that no team received special engines or preferential treatment, and there was a minimum standard that every unit had to reach before it was let out after build or rebuild. Spears was set to service two customer car teams plus four chassis builders: Cooper, Lotus, Brabham and Lola. Both Brabham and Lola were new to Formula One.

Lola boss Eric Broadley had made his name designing sports cars and had been commissioned to produce a Formula One chassis for the two car Reg Parnell run-Bowmaker/Yeoman Credit team. Brabham, of course, was no stranger to Formula One and had left the Cooper team to exploit his 'Motor Racing Developments' partnership with designer Ron Tauranac. Since the first Brabham-Tauranac (BT series) Formula One car would not be ready for the start of the season Brabham put in an order for a new Lotus. UDT-Laystall also purchased new Lotus chassis, and both Climax and BRM V8 engines. The other Climax customer was Rob Walker, Moss' entrant.

Both Lotus and Cooper ran on Esso which precluded BP driver Stirling Moss from driving for them. The Esso retainer was a major source of team income and Moss continued with the Walker team running a Lotus 18/21 rather than the newer Type 24 chassis in view of the fuel company conflict. However, he was slated to drive a UDT-Laystall 24 in selected non-championship Formula One races.

Chapman's policy for 1962 was to make Lotus Formula One chassis available to existing customers only, thereby confining total production to a maximum of 15 cars. Demand came from teams involved in national as well as international racing - for example there was a strong market in South Africa. There were three basic versions in existence: the Type 21 four cylinder chassis, an 'interim' version of the 21 with a widened chassis to accept a Climax or BRM V8 engine and the brand new Type 24 which had been designed specifically to accept a V8. The 24 was essentially a sleeker version of the 21 with certain suspension refinements and was destined for World Championship races.

While Chapman was prepared to sell these tubular frame models to approved customers he was not planning to offer his clients the still secret monocoque chassis car under development for the factory team. The radical Type 25 was a step into the unknown, a potential world beater and a possible flop. Team Lotus had so far only won one World Championship race, the final round of the 1961 season at Watkins Glen. It had yet to establish itself as a major force in the Grand Prix arena, though the excellence of

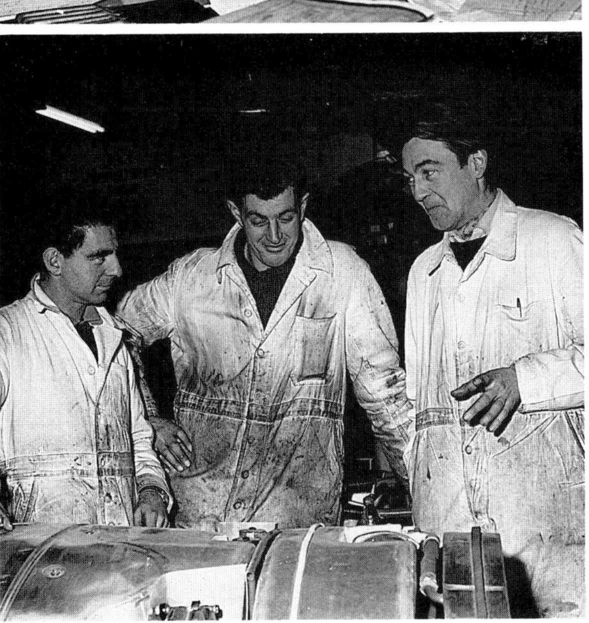

*otus' Cheshunt base in 962 and some of its key gures including echnical Director Mike ostin (at his desk) and olin Chapman (in nglasses) with Jimmy lark. The mechanics are edric Selzer (left), Jim ndruweit and David azenby (centre)*

Chapman's mid engined chassis approach was widely recognised. The new multi tubular frame 24 was Chapman's fail safe, should the 25 prove a step too far.

Working under Chapman, the Group Lotus Technical Director was Mike Costin, brother of aerodynamic expert Frank. In the Fifties Frank Costin had worked as Vanwall and Lotus' aerodynamicist while Mike had set up a racing engine company with Keith Duckworth, which they dubbed Cosworth. Duckworth now worked full time for Cosworth, Costin for Lotus where he was responsible for the development of both passenger and racing cars. The latter included sports-racing and Formula Junior as well as Formula One machines.

The Lotus road and racing cars were designed and built within the same complex at Delamare Road, Cheshunt. This was the modest facility to which Lotus Cars Ltd had moved in the late Fifties from North London, where it had been born behind the Railway Hotel in Hornsey Lane. Stan Chapman, Landlord of the Railway Hotel administered his son's racing team with Andrew Ferguson Team Manager while Fred Bushell held the purse strings as Commercial Manager of Lotus Cars and Team Lotus.

Lotus' Chief Draughtsman was Alan Styman and he was assisted by Ian Jones, Bill Webb, Paul Wright, Mike Wardle and David Shuttle. They drew road as well as racing cars. Typically, Chapman drew the overall scheme for a new car, leaving the drawing office to fill in the details. Sometimes racing car parts were improvised by the Team mechanics - who built their own cars - and such parts were later recorded by the drawing office. Team Lotus' Chief Mechanic was Jim Endruweit and his race crew included Dick Scammell, Ted Woodley, David Lazenby and Cedric Selzer while Derek Wilde looked after the engines and transmissions.

'Glen victor Innes Ireland had been dropped from the '62 factory line up, to make room for Formula Junior Champion Trevor Taylor while promising Grand Prix newcomer Jim Clark indisputably headed the team. Both Taylor and Clark had found tremendous Formula Junior success driving for Chapman and Clark's recent Formula One speed belied his lack of experience. At first the brace of British Racing Green machines from Cheshunt comprised 24 models, the 25 not scheduled to race before the Grand Prix season got underway in May.

Team Lotus ran a very full season, taking in many of the non-championship events that these days put around 30 races annually on the Formula One calendar. Of course, the financial inducement had to be sufficient. Starting and prize money was another important source of Team income, as was the sale of Formula One, Formula Two and Formula Junior chassis and spare parts. Aside from the substantial Esso retainer, cash and product assistance was received from other suppliers such as Dunlop, Girling and Champion. Usually remuneration was success related.

Vic Barlow headed the Dunlop Formula One racing service while Jack Leonard looked after Sports-Prototypes. Both of them participated in R5 tyre design work and thus had a direct hand in the products their trucks dispensed.

Esso's involvement was overseen by Reg Tanner. Tanner had done much to restore good relations between Chapman and Climax boss Leonard Lee following rows over the FWE engine supplied for Lotus Cars' Elite production model. It was the deterioration in the relationship between Coventry and Cheshunt that had seen Cooper and Rob Walker rather than Team Lotus run the prototype FWMV engines. On the driver front, Climax had particularly high regard for Jack Brabham, who could provide strong technical feedback.

For its racing gearboxes Lotus had forged an exclusive relationship with ZF, having abandoned attempts to produce its own unit. ZF - Zahnradfabrik Friedrichshafen AG - had for years supplied the Formula One field with its limited slip differential. It produced the four speed gearbox used in the Elite and that connection had led Lotus to the Formula One deal. Within the ZF range Chapman had found the ideal basis for a five speed racing unit in an experimental four speed unit intended for a front wheel drive industrial application. Essentially this was reworked to sit upside down at the rear of a Formula One car (with the gear cluster outrigged behind the differential). All 21 models had employed the so called 5DS10 which continued into 1962.

The prototype Lotus 24 (chassis 948) made its debut in Clark's hands at Brussels on April 1, the World Championship season and the debut of the Type 25 still some way off. Only Clark and Moss (in the Walker car) ran Climax V8 engines in Belgium and both retired with valve train failure. However, two weeks later at Snetterton Clark won following Moss' retirement with a broken throttle cable. That was Moss' last event before his accident.

On April 23 Moss contested the Lavant Trophy at Goodwood, Clark the more prestigious Pau Grand Prix. In France Clark started from pole and led until struck by a gear selection malady. In England Moss mysteriously crashed following gear selection delays, while trying to better the fastest lap set by Surtees' new V8 Lola-Climax.

A week later at Aintree Clark's 24-FWMV was uncatchable, then Graham Hill's BRM-V8 pipped it at the post in the International Trophy at Silverstone, profiting from a late shower. With Moss in hospital and Ferrari (still led by Phil Hill and with '61 V6 cars) apparently lagging in the face of the new generation British V8s, Clark, Hill and Surtees (third at Silverstone) were shaping up as favourites for the World Championship, with Brabham the dark horse. Ginther supported Hill at BRM while McLaren and Maggs represented Cooper, Gurney and Bonnier Porsche. Battle commenced one week after the International Trophy, over at Zandvoort in Holland...

# Small Port Success

**FWMV V-8**
**90 degree V8**
**63.0 x 60.0mm. /1495.0cc.**
**Unblown**
**Aluminium alloy block and heads**
**Wet cast iron liners**
**5 main bearings, plain**
**Steel crankshaft, 4 pins**
**Steel con rods**
**Brico light alloy pistons**
**AE rings**
**D.o.h.c., chain driven**
**2 valves/cylinder, 1 plug**
**60 degree included valve angle**
**34.29mm. inlet valve, 31.75mm. exhaust**
**Lucas ignition**
**4 Weber carburettors**
**Compression ratio 11.5:1**
**122 kg (with starter and alternator).**

**Maximum r.p.m. 8,500**
**Stroke:bore ratio 0.952:1**
**Piston area 34sq.in.**
**Maximum piston acceleration (8,500r.p.m.)**
**97,800ft.sec.$^2$**

Coventry Climax Engines Ltd, the company of which Leonard Lee was Chairman, Managing Director and major shareholder, was a substantial manufacturer of fire pumps, fork lift trucks and small industrial engines in 1962. It had first dabbled in the world of Grand Prix racing a decade earlier. Lee was a racing enthusiast and had as Chief Engineer Walter Hassan, a one time Bentley racing mechanic, Brooklands special builder and more recently joint creator of the Le Mans winning Jaguar XK six cylinder engine. In 1953 Hassan had as Chief Designer Harry Mundy: he had worked on ERA engine design and after the war had been involved in the BRM V16 project. Both Hassan and Mundy were likewise racing enthusiasts.

Following the announcement of the move to 2.5 litre Formula One Cooper, Connaught and other British racing car constructors had asked Lee to assign Hassan and Mundy the development of a suitable engine. Although this project duly went ahead, it was as a spare time activity. In 1953 a V8 unit emerged and it was subsequently coaxed to produce in excess of 260b.h.p., a highly competitive figure. Alas, Climax was misled by the exaggerated power claims of rival manufacturers and consequently the part time exercise fizzled out.

Hassan and Mundy were very busy at this stage with regular industrial work and a sports-racing engine. They had already jointly developed a lightweight one litre fire pump engine, the FW, which first ran in 1951. The FW - feather weight - was an all aluminium-alloy in line four with wedge heads and parallel valves operated through bucket tappets by a single overhead camshaft. Given the identity of its parents it was not surprising that it should have inherent tuning potential. While Hassan and Mundy had been busy siring the 2.5 litre V8 various constructors requested a race prepared version of the FW for the 1.1 litre sports car class.

The so called FWA emerged in 1954 and soon became the dominant force in small capacity sports car racing. The later enlarged capacity FWB version continued this success in the 1.5 litre class. Hence the famous slogan 'the fire pump that wins races'! In 1956 the FWB was used by Cooper in a Formula Two car, this move paving the way for the twin cam FPF Formula Two engine. The FPF engine was Climax' first real racing engine to see action and it was closely based on the still born 2.5 litre V8 (dubbed FPE).

Mundy having left in 1955, the FPF was developed by Hassan assisted by Peter Windsor-Smith. The purpose designed 1.5 litre Formula Two racing engine was stretched to 2.2 litres to provide a 1958 Formula One power plant for Cooper and thus Climax went Grand Prix racing in an unplanned fashion. Like the FPE, the two valve, twin cam FPF had a 66 degree included valve angle and a pent roof head working in conjunction with a pent roof piston crown. Again the valves were operated through bucket tappets. Both head and block-cum-crankcase were naturally aluminium alloy and pushed to 2.2 litres for Formula One, the cylinder dimensions went from over-square to square.

Following two Grand Prix wins, for 1959 Hassan redesigned the crankcase to stand up to the strain of a full 2.5 litre capacity. Revised, bigger valve heads followed while bore and stroke dimensions of 94.0 x 89.9mm. gave the 2.5 litre displacement (2495cc.), these dimensions dictated by the logistics of enlargement and the desire to return to an over-square engine. The big valve FPF enjoyed high b.m.e.p. but ran to less than 8,000r.p.m. producing virtually 100b.h.p. per litre on the regulation Avgas.

Its valve sizes were still somewhat small relative to the norm for its bore size in the interest of a good spread of power while its speed was badly constrained by considerations of stress. Taken to 8,00Cr.p.m. its tappets and con rod bolts became undependable. Nevertheless, with 250b.h.p, good driveability and light weight the FPF became the Champion engine in 2.5 litre Grand Prix racing, Cooper winning the 1959 and '60 World titles with the help of driver-cum-mechanic Jack Brabham and its pioneering mid engine chassis configuration.

The Formula Two FPF was, of course, the engine Climax employed as a stop gap in the early days of the 1.5 litre Formula One. This smaller engine could run a little faster. Although in 1961 Mark II trim respectably producing just over 100b.h.p. per litre on five star, its output was woefully inadequate given that the Ferrari V6 produced a genuine 120b.h.p. per litre. The go-ahead for a new, higher speed clean sheet of paper design had not been given until 1960, over a year after the announcement of the new Formula. The problem was that Climax' customers had refused to accept the change, campaigning vehemently for a retention of 2.5 litres...

Ever the practical engineer, Hassan felt that eight cylinders would provide sufficient power with the benefits of light weight, ease of chassis installation and good fuel economy. A compact, relatively simple 90 degree V8 fitted the bill. It would retain the basic concept that had led to the success of the FPF series, design and development concentrating upon power characteristics as much as peak output. Hassan explained the philosophy thus, in a 1966 presentation to the S.A.E:

'Modern Grand Prix circuits vary considerably, some placing a premium upon acceleration, others upon maximum speed. However, if the use of engine performance is studied relative to the various circuits, it is evident that the time during which the car operates at maximum r.p.m. and power is extremely small, compared with the time spent accelerating in order to reach this maximum, only to commence braking for the next bend. The most successful engine is, therefore, the one which combines a good maximum power with exceptional torque spread over at least 2,500r.p.m. or, better still, 3,500r.p.m.

'Under these conditions the driver will have a far less fatiguing time, because gear changing will become less exacting and he will have more time to deal with the actual driving of the car, that is, steering, braking and the like. It has been our policy to produce engines possessing good torque characteristics in the middle speed range. To achieve this is impossible if valves and ports of unlimited size are used in order to achieve the highest maximum power regardless of other requirements.

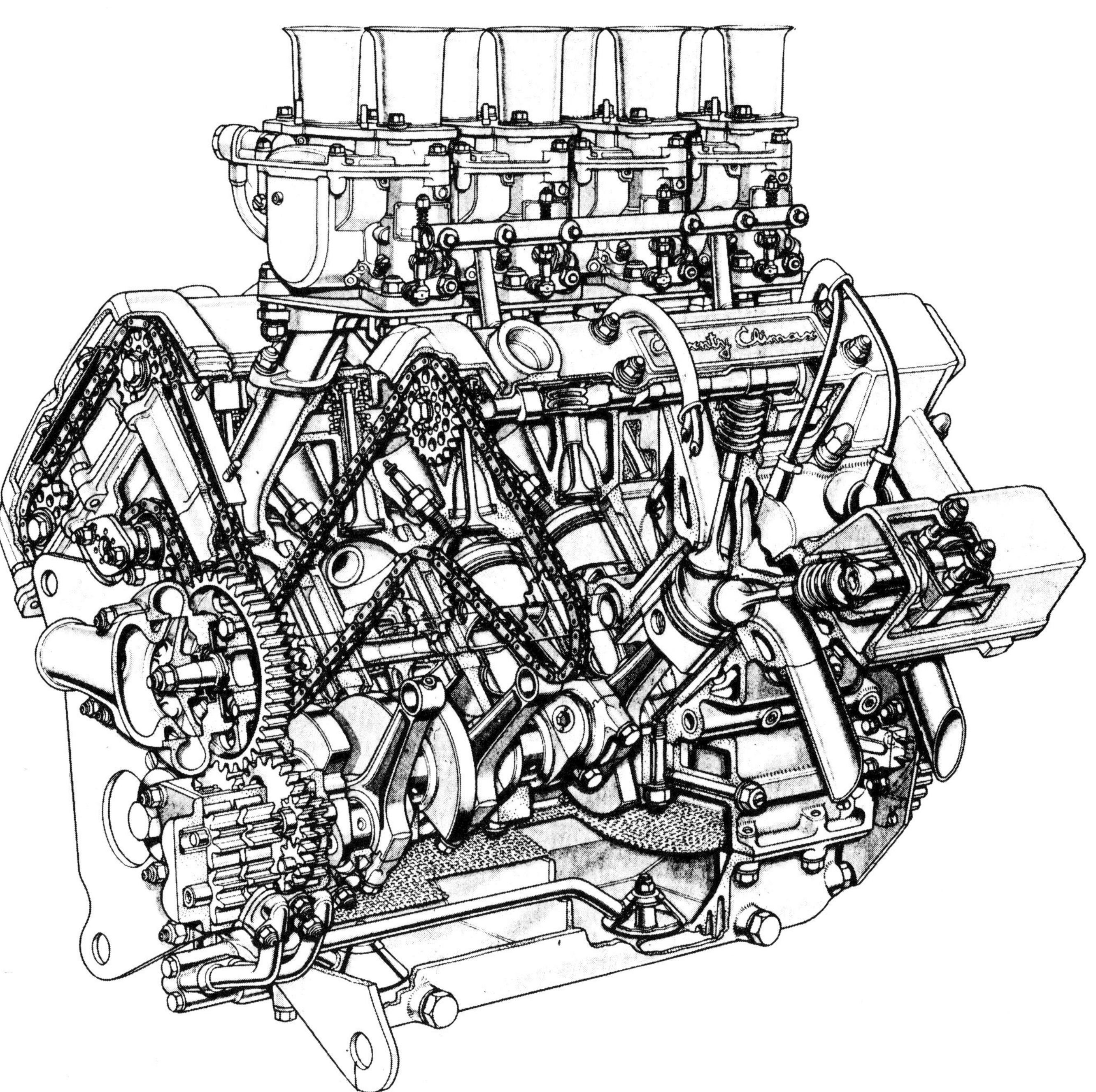


'The Coventry Climax approach is, therefore, to incorporate the smallest valves and ports from which adequate power can be obtained, since this does allow maximum torque to be developed below the speed of maximum power and a high compression ratio assists considerably in compensating for the slight lack of breathing at maximum speed'.

In line with this philosophy, Hassan decided to start with the proven stroke:bore ratio of the FPF, looking to the significantly smaller cylinder dimensions of a 1.5 litre V8 to reduce inertia stresses and hence increase useable engine speed. Climax had already produced an engine with similar size cylinders in the so called FWM series and this was used to test piston and port design.

The first FWM - 'feather weight marine' - engine was a version of the original single cam FW fire pump engine that was smaller and lighter thanks as much to accumulated knowledge as to its displacement of only 742cc. This diminutive boat engine sired the FWMA: A for automotive. The racing version of that was the twin cam FWMC used by Lotus at Le Mans in 1961.

Hassan noted in his autobiography 'Climax in Coventry' (ISBN 0 900549 28 9) that, 'various people have suggested that the V8 was really just a doubling up of the FWMC, but this is not really true. Certainly we used the basic porting, valve gear, camshaft drive and cylinder head details from the FWMC, but the bore and stoke were different, the cylinder block construction was revised to allow open deck casting, and most important, we used a five bearing crank instead of the FWMC's three bearing crank, and stretched the engine to accommodate the extra big ends. So the cylinder centres were not even the same as on the FWMC, and the cylinder heads consequently were not interchangeable.'

The FWMC was merely a starting point for the new V8, its 82.5b.h.p. at 8,200r.p.m. from 742cc. equating to a useful 170b.h.p. from 1.5 litres. Hassan told the S.A.E: 'Initially we did not think it wise to aim at too great an increase in r.p.m, and we also considered that a very much over-square stroke:bore ratio would involve a difficult and lengthy development period which, of course, we could not afford... One major difficulty with a large bore is the provision of a sufficiently high compression ratio with a smooth and compact combustion chamber. The provision of sufficient valve to piston clearance, using the large degree of valve overlap necessary for high speed operation, results in deep cavities in the piston crowns.

'We therefore settled for a conservative peak crankshaft speed of 8,500r.p.m. which, with a bore and stroke of 2.48 and 2.36in. (63 and 60.0mm.) respectively, together with a con rod centre distance of 4.2in. gave a maximum piston acceleration of 97,800ft.sec.$^2$

As a measure of stress, piston acceleration needs to be considered in the context of bore size, the bore size a guide to the relevant inertia mass. By way of comparison, the 2.5 litre FPF experienced maximum piston acceleration of 94,000ft.sec.$^2$ at 6,800r.p.m. and given its 95mm. bore that rate of acceleration represented a significantly higher stress level (in spite of the lower engine speed, it should be noted).

Of rival engines, the BRM V8 was much more highly stressed that the FWMV having a maximum piston acceleration of 125,000ft.sec.$^2$ at 10,500r.p.m. and a bore size of 68.5mm. However, the big valve version of the Ferrari V6 was even more highly stressed, having a maximum piston acceleration of 132,000ft.sec.$^2$ at 10,000r.p.m. and a bore size of 72mm. Yet arguably the Ferrari was not as highly stressed on this comparative basis as the 1958 World Championship winning Vanwall four which had a maximum piston acceleration of 105,500 ft.sec.$^2$ at 7,400r.p.m. and a bore size of 96mm.

The FWMV's four cylinder origins did not lead Hassan to run it as a pair of four cylinder engines sharing a flat plane four cylinder-type crankshaft. Hassan opted for a conventional 90 degree V8 two plane crank, albeit still with rods paired on four con rod journals. An early difficulty was caused by the churning of oil in the crankcase by the crankshaft and con rods. A sizable gain in power was achieved by lowering the sump 50mm. Various forms of baffle were tried and eventually a copper gauze screen arranged to follow the path of the big ends solved the problem, allowing the sump to be raised again by 36mm. Hassan speculated that the screen was acting as a non-return valve, protecting the oil from the windage effect of the rotating components.

Using a two plane crank, it transpired that exhaust impulses were awkwardly spaced when it came to exhaust system pulse tuning. Since individual cylinder stack pipes provided good power only within a very narrow rev band Climax had to look to pipe blending. This did not produce results until the inner pair of cylinders on each bank was interconnected with the outer pair on the other bank. Only by this means could even exhaust pulses be fed into each of two tail pipes.

Since the induction tracts were set within the vee, the exhaust manifolding outside and under the heads, it was a layout that would have been impossible given the shorter primaries required for higher speed running. Given the speed Climax was running the required pipe crossover system was just about feasible, resorting to some very tight bends in the primaries as they hugged the heads, running to meet over the bellhousing. Those bends did not appear to affect the exhaust tuning and the complex system produced better engine performance than any other layout. However, it left a nightmare of plumbing to confront the chassis builder.

Following the FWM pattern, FWMV enjoyed notably straight downdraught inlet ports with little curvature at the seat, this arrangement known to promote good breathing. Following the advice of a consultant, Hassan had initially run a modified port with an increase of bore adjacent to the valve seat which increased the flow rate but in this form power output was poor. Not until the port was sleeved back down to follow the FWMC pattern had the projected output been achieved. Hassan suggests this was due to the change of area before the valve seat upsetting the inlet ram conditions, 'probably by constituting some form of pneumatic spring, which dissipated the dynamic energy of the column of intake gas in the port'.

With its inlet and exhaust properly tuned for a wide spread of power the FWMV provided its maximum torque at 78% of its peak power speed, just like the '54/'55 Mercedes W196 straight eight and the '56/'57 Maserati 250F in line six. That peak power speed was the maximum 8,500r.p.m. and the output was registered as 174b.h.p. prior to any track running. The attention to a wide power band explains the moderate valve lift - 0.36in. on both sides - and the mild valve timing: inlet opens 45 degrees BTDC, closes 65 degrees ABDC; exhaust opens 65 degrees BBDC, closes 45 degrees ATDC.

Power was strong from 6,000 to 8,500r.p.m. and by August the output was up to 181b.h.p. at maximum speed with torque quoted as 118lb.ft. at 7,500r.p.m. Already, at this early stage, the overall engine performance compared favourably to that of the dominating V6 Ferrari engine. The prototype went into its first race following only hasty tests at Silverstone, powering Jack Brabham's Cooper in the '61 German Grand Prix on the Nurburgring. Brabham had been having a poor season but he put the 530kg. V8 Cooper straight onto the front row, just a fraction off Phil Hill's Ferrari pole time.

Alas, a water loss problem bugged the prototype unit, and in any case Brabham spun out on the first lap due to inappropriate tyres. Two prototype units appeared at Monza, for Brabham and Moss but the water loss problem persisted. Indeed, it persisted to the end of the season. Brabham led for over half the US Grand Prix finale only to be struck down by the ailment. It was not until Climax rigged up a full car-type sealed cooling system in the Coventry dyno room that the root of the problem - unencountered in previous bench testing - was finally identified.

It was discovered that combustion gases were entering the water, pressurising the radiator system and that this was causing the water loss. It was not a straightforward case of cylinder head gaskets blowing but was a problem caused by the unusual architecture of the new engine.

The FWMV had each cast iron wet liner seated on a ledge at the bottom of the water jacket and sealed with O rings and not supported radially at the top by the alloy block, which was of open deck construction. The upper flange of each liner was clamped by the head with a Cooper ring providing a seal. The Cooper ring was a laminated metal sealing ring made by Coopers Mechanical Joint Co. Ltd. and consisted of a pack of narrow rings contained within a spun casing, the rings of stainless steel and Nimonic material. The water joint was completed by an asbestos type jointing material.

The sealing ring failure arose through a differential in the expansion of the 75mm. of liner between the head and its seating flange compared to the expansion, or lack of it of the block. Hassan noted, 'this was probably accentuated by the fact that since the water temperature remained relatively constant the height of the aluminium block also remained constant whereas the cast iron liner was subject to temperature changes due to firing conditions, that is, throttle open, throttle closed'.

When the engine cooled as the throttle was lifted the differential effect was sufficient to relieve the Cooper ring of clamping loads, allowing it to shuffle. The problem was overcome by replacing the liner seating flange with an aluminium sleeve, sealing into the base of the block and supporting the liner under an upper flange. Thus, the engine became of dry liner construction. At the same time it was switched to closed deck construction and its cooling problem was overcome.

The water loss problem solved, Climax could commence production of the 16 customer engines required for the 1962 season. These were supplied at a cost of £3000 each, compared to

£2250 for an FPF. As we have seen, the '62-spec. made it entrance at Brussels and won at Snetterton second time out in Clark's hands (this in fact the '61 Brabham prototype engine uprated and on loan from the Development 'Shop).

The power output of the so called Mark II version which featured 1.35 rather than 1.30in. inlet valves, retaining 1.237in. exhaust valves was 186b.h.p. at 8,500r.p.m. Torque was 119.3lb.ft. at 7,500r.p.m. and power was still very strong from 6,000r.p.m., Climax ensuring a flexible engine. It claimed a specific fuel consumption of only 0.594pt./b.h.p./hr. at maximum r.p.m.

The heart of the new V8 was a classic hemispherical head combustion chamber run in conjunction with a domed piston crown having only light valve clearance notches. A single central plug was provided and the valves were inclined symmetrically, each at 30 degrees from the vertical. They were operated directly via twin overhead camshafts through bucket tappets with shim adjustment. Twin coil springs closed each valve.

Three ring light alloy pistons running in the cast iron liners drove a five bearing crankshaft through I-section steel con-rods. The crankshaft turned in plain bearings with the timing drive taken from its front end. A spur gear on the shaft turned another above it, the latter turning a jackshaft at half engine speed. The shaft ran down the valley of the monobloc. Right behind the jackshaft's drive gear, a pair of sprockets provided a chain drive for each bank. Adjustment of the single 3/8″ pitch Reynolds roller chain was via the adjustable jockey sprocket set in front of each bank.

The ignition distributor was driven by skew gears off the rear of the jackshaft, the water pump off its nose. The oil pressure pump was driven from the front of the crankshaft and oil was fed into each main bearing from a large diameter gallery bored, from end to end, in the side of the crankcase. The pressure pump fed the oil to a short drilling, via a pressure relief valve and then to a cartridge-type oil filter which was bolted to a facing on the side of the crankcase. The filtered oil then passed to the crankcase gallery.

The engine employed a light aluminium alloy (LM8WP) combined block and crankcase sand casting which extended from the decks to below the main bearing caps. The main bearing caps were of steel with intermediate and centre caps attached to the crankcase walls via horizontal bolts, producing a notably rigid bottom end structure. The FWMV was designed for rigid mounting into a chassis without the danger of crankcase distortion and consequent misalignment of the main bearings.

Six bolt holes, four on the front cover and two at the rear cover were picked up by the chassis. The front end of the engine was not lengthened unnecessarily by accessories so that it could be mounted close to the firewall bulkhead at the back of the cockpit. That helped Chapman and his followers recline the driver without extending the wheelbase unduly. The transaxle bolted directly to the rear cover which incorporated the bellhousing, the clutch meeting a small, low mounted flywheel. The crankshaft flywheel was the same 216mm. diameter as the clutch adapter ring.

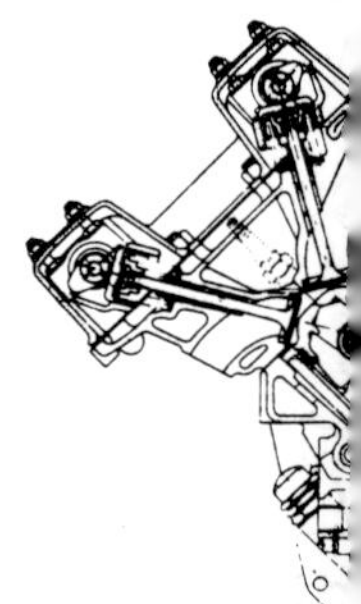

The two plane crankshaft set front and rear pins at 90 degrees to the centre pair which were 180 degrees apart. It was of nickel-chrome molybdenum steel (EN24V) with full counterbalancing webs opposite each throw equalling the appropriate reciprocating mass and extra balance weights at the front end to counteract the inherent rocking couple of a V8 with a two plane crankshaft. The oil seal at the rear of the crankshaft was of the piston ring type.

The crankshaft drilling was arranged so that the oil feed was continuous end to end, assisting the balance of feed to the big end bearings despite the possible variation in leak-off at the various bearings. The feed to the big end bearings was via holes drilled through both sides of the crankpin at 90 degrees to the t.d.c. position.

Both Vandervell lead indium and Glacier aluminium rectilinear tin bearings were used in the engine, the mains and big end bearings being Vandervell VP2. The main bearings were of 2.0in. diameter with the intermediates 0.7in. wide, the others 0.8in. wide. The big end bearings were of 1.625in. diameter and 0.75in. width.

The heads were made of the same alloy as the monobloc with austenitic cast iron valve seats shrunk in. The inlet valve material was a widely used chromium-nickel-iron alloy, 'XB', while

*Team Lotus first ran the Climax V8 in a Type 24 chassis. These shots show Clark's example at Silverstone in May while the cross-section is of the engine. Awaiting the Type 25, Clark had earlier won with the FWMV-24 at Snetterton and Aintree, here he was second.*

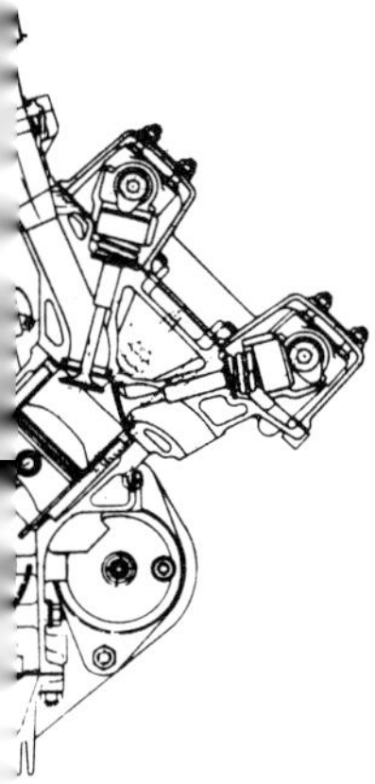

the exhaust valves were of 21-4NS. The camshafts ran in five bearings, originally being steel with cast iron tappets but in '62 changed for chilled iron with steel tappets. The camshafts were supported in castings which also served as tappet blocks. Running directly in the aluminium tappet block, the bucket tappets made provision for shim adjustment of valve clearance.

The pistons were supplied by Brico and were sand cast in aluminium alloy and X-rayed for cracks, each weighing 8oz. 15grs. The top ring was a Dykes-type L-section compression ring under which were a taper-faced plain ring and a typical U-section oil scraper ring. All rings were cast iron. The gudgeon pins were circlip located. The con rods were 4.2in. centre to centre and were drop-forged in nickel-chrome steel and machine finished. Horizontally-split big ends were secured by 0.375in. screws. Each con rod weighed 16oz. 6grs.

The water pump was of the double volute

type, with a separate outlet for each bank. The oil pumps were set in tandem, with the pressure pump set on the front main bearing panel behind the gear drive from the crank and driven by spur gears at 0.7 engine speed. Two separate scavenge pumps were located on the outside of the timing drive cover plate and were connected to the driven gear by means of an Oldhams coupling. These pumps separately scavenged the front and rear of the crankcase and had a combined capacity of twice the pressure pump.

Ignition was via the Lucas transistorised system which was well capable of supplying the 567 sparks per second required at 8,500r.p.m. since its potential was up to 1000 per second without a voltage drop. Timing was controlled by pole pieces on the back of the flywheel running in conjunction with an electromagnetic pick up on the engine backplate. The system also comprised a pulse shaping network based on a Schmitt trigger circuit, a spark generator and a high tension distributor. All the electronic units used germanium transistors, and were encapsulated in a silica-filled epoxy resin to provide support against vibrational effects. Single 10mm. plugs were employed while consistent battery voltage was ensured by the use of a Lucas alternator. The alternator was from a motorcycle design and was set to the front of the engine on the righthand side, driven by a vee belt from the nose of the crankshaft.

As the crankshaft rotated a voltage impulse was produced at the pick up each time one of the accurately positioned pole pieces passed within the pick up field. This pulse was amplified by the trigger circuit. Effectively, this was a normally closed switch which allowed battery current to flow through the primary of a trigger transformer situated in the spark generator. The amplified pulse had the effect of "opening" this switch, so that current flow in the transformer primary winding ceased.

The energy released by the resulting collapse of current induced a voltage in the trigger transformer secondary winding and this in turn caused current to flow in the base circuit of a transistor in the spark generator. The transistor thereby became conducting and battery current flowed in the primary winding of a high voltage transformer, this circuit being arranged to initiate a regenerative effect. Consequently, primary current rose very rapidly to a value of about 80 amperes, giving rise to an induced voltage in the transformer secondary of the order of 20kV.

This spark supply was fed to a conventional rotor arm for distribution. Regeneration ceased when the transformer was saturated, and the transistor again became non-conducting. With the cessation of the voltage pulse at the pick up, the trigger amplifier switch again closed and conduction recommenced in the trigger transformer primary in readiness for the cycle - which occupied less than 200 microseconds - to be repeated at the next pick up pulse.

The new 'spark box' was finned for cooling and it was important to put it out in the airstream to keep it cool: the system was known to abruptly stop working following overheating of the 'box. Further, in these early days the transistor system didn't work well at very low speed. However, the spark was produced almost instantly when commanded by the trigger pulse and had a constant value independent of speed.

The four carburettors were twin choke Weber DCNL-4 Type 38 fitted with 32mm. choke tubes, having originally been preferred 38 IDFs, supply of which had simply dried up. In general, the Weber twin choke racing carburettor was a straightforward design and it was actually two complete units sharing a common float chamber. On all versions, much attention was paid to aerodynamic design to avoid pressure loss through the choke tube.

Compared to the V8 seen in Clark's early season Type 24, the FWMV for the Type 25 boasted an improved induction system. The four Webers were mounted transversely and in a row, this arrangement providing the scope for improved inlet passages and a simplified throttle linkage system. However, there remained the drawback that, since each carburettor had to be installed across the vee the float chamber was considerably ahead of the jets and choke tubes, this causing tuning difficulties especially when accelerating out of corners at part throttle.

The complex 'spaghetti pipe' exhaust system was nickel bronze welded and involved some tricky tube manipulation, this work undertaken by V.W. Derrington Ltd, liaising with the relevant chassis manufacturer.

*The colour photograph on the next eight pag show Clark's Clima FWMV – Lotus 25 i action during 196 The photographs sho – in order – Clark a Zandvoort, chasin Brabham's Clima FWMV-Lotus 24 a Monaco, at the Rheim start, in the 'Ring Karasell and at Eas London. At Rheims th four strong front ro comprises McLaren Climax-Cooper (in fact coming through from th second row), the Clar Lotus, Hill's BRM an Surtees' Climax-Lol*

MARTINI

BP
18
22

BP
DUNLOP
ENERGOL
BP
ENERGOL
DUNLOP

TOTAL TOTAL

5

# True Inspiration

**Team Lotus aluminium monocoque**
**Semi-stressed engine**
**Rocker arm front suspension, outboard rear**
**Armstrong dampers**
**Lotus magnesium 15″ rims**
**Girling 10.5″ diameter cast iron discs, outboard**
**Girling single, two pot calipers, Ferodo pads**
**G.r.p. bodywork**
**1 Serck combined water and oil radiator**
**AP 7 1/4″ twin plate clutch**
**ZF 5 speed gearbox, ZF l.s.d.**
**118 litre fuel tank, 11 litre oil tank**
**Varley battery, Smiths instruments**
**2286mm. wheelbase; 1346mm. front track, 1372mm. rear**
**452kg.**

When the transporters rolled in through the gates of the sandy, wind swept Zandvoort circuit with its numerous seafood stalls there was generally thought to be little difference in chassis technology between the key V8-engined cars produced by Lotus, Lola and BRM. BRM continued to rely upon its '61 chassis V8 car while the new Lotus 24 and Lola V8 designs were not radical departures from that conventional multi-tubular machine. If BRM threatened higher peak power with its higher revs, the Climax V8 offered a more useable spread of power. On balance, the favourites looked evenly matched, all running on exactly the same Dunlop tyres. Then Team Lotus opened the doors of its transporter and out was proudly pushed a new factor in the performance equation: the stressed-skin monocoque-type chassis structure.

A chassis exists primarily to carry the other elements of a car - the engine, the transmission, the suspension, the bodywork and so forth. The traditional ladder frame did this well enough - it was strong and it was efficient since it was a light structure. Rigid it was not, however, and lack of rigidity became of serious concern following the move to independent suspension.

Independent suspension exerted a much higher torsional loading. When leaf springs had carried a beam axle, the springs - particularly at the front - had tended to be well inboard. With independent suspension the distance between spring centres increased to approximately the width of the track. It followed that when a wheel on one side rose over a bump, the resultant upward thrust exerted on the frame had much greater leverage about the longitudinal axis of the car. As we have already noted, to work effectively independent suspension needs its chassis mounts to be firmly anchored in relationship to one another. Clearly, high chassis rigidity was a prerequisite for the sophisticated suspension necessary to get the most out of the high co-efficient tyres that emerged from the Fifties.

Since suspension loads are 'point' loads a tubular frame should be well suited to handling them but if it is to offer adequate rigidity the structure must be properly triangulated. The ideal is a pure spaceframe in which all tubes are arranged so as to be free from bending loads. To achieve this within the constraints of a Formula One chassis would require such complex and complete triangulation that none of the resultant apertures could possibly be large enough to allow driver access. Provide a suitable cockpit aperture and stiffness deteriorates markedly: the rigidity of the whole is that of the weakest area.

With the development of independent suspension for racing cars came development of the heavily triangulated yet unavoidably compromised multi-tubular frame. In view of the compromise not all designers looked to extensive triangulation. For example, the 1961 Ferrari featured little triangulation and used large section heavy gauge tubing to help compensate. Meanwhile, in the aircraft world the monocoque fuselage had logically ousted a combination of tubular frame and shape-giving non-structural skin.

On an aircraft the loading is mainly aerodynamic and as such tends to be spread evenly over a large area. In view of that designers dispensed with a combination of complex frame and non-structural clothing, instead using a metal skin between stiffening ribs to resist shear and axial forces. The skin was formed like a shell which for strength was kept as completely closed as possible. Everything was attached to it by brackets designed to spread loads over a wide area. Properly engineered, the monocoque fuselage was lighter and it could be more rigid in bending and in torsion for a given weight.

The principle of monocoque construction was not so readily applicable to a racing car chassis since the problem here was essentially one of high point rather than more even loading and there had to be that proportionally larger opening in the 'fuselage' through which to insert the driver, not to mention access for the engine. Then there was the problem of service access, while a convenient multi-tubular frame with separate body panels offered the freedom to play with alternative forms of streamlining. The single seater racing car fuselage logically was inspired by spaceframe rather than monocoque construction technique.

Of course, over the years there were ever those keen to try to adapt monocoque technology to the single seater racing car chassis. For example, BRM tried to incorporate a monocoque centre section in a mid Fifties fuselage, though a full length frame had to be retained to ensure sufficient strength in the cockpit area. One can cite many other examples, such as the 1915 Cornelian Indianapolis car, the 1923 Voisin Grand Prix car, the 1949 Trimax 500cc racer, and so on and so on. Colin Chapman did not invent the idea of a single seater of monocoque construction, he showed how it should be done. Chapman devised an entirely practical form of monocoque construction for the single seater racing car - we shall call his creation the monocoque tub.

Since the rigidity of a tube increases at a significantly greater rate for any increase in diameter, it follows that designers had always aspired to the concept of a single large diameter thinwall tube as the ideal basis for the ultimate single seater fuselage. Alas, since there was no way to overcome the problem of the cockpit opening this train of thought had not led anywhere. Chapman, on the other hand, had recognised that two smaller tubes set in parallel either side of the engine and the cockpit could each offer enough section for adequate stiffness while accommodating much of the 25 gallons so of fuel required by the new breed of V8 engine.

Front and rear bulkheads, a semi stressed engine and various other components such as the roll hoop, the dash hoop and the cockpit floor could be called upon to hold these tubes rigidly in parallel. Better still, they needed to extend no further than the heads of a 90 degree V8 engine. Fuel accommodation was a major headache in the conventional tubular chassis - the latest V8 cars setting a massive aluminium container over the driver's legs - and Chapman now had a solution in a clever chassis structure which left the cockpit area as strong as the rest of the car, the fuel set low and the fuselage no wider than necessary. With a non-structural top section closing the fuselage the aerodynamic form could be easily altered and service access was not a problem. Indeed, it was facilitated.

Mike Costin recalls how the idea came to Chapman in the course of a regular lunchtime meeting between the two of them, with Lotus buyer John Standen also in attendance. The lunch was at a restaurant in Waltham Abbey High Street and as was often the case ways of engineering the team's Formula One cars was the topic under discussion. Costin says that Chapman's monocoque tub idea was not a premeditated one: "it just happened - Colin literally sketched it out on a paper napkin". They talked through the concept and methods of manufacture, drawing on Costin's background in the aircraft industry. Then Chapman went straight home and drew up the general scheme of the Lotus 25, launching a revolution in Grand Prix car design.

The new tub echoed the general layout of the wooden monocoque incorporated in a Marcos sports car designed by Costin's brother Frank a year earlier. However, with monocoque technology common in road cars - Chapman's own Elite had a g.r.p. monocoque - this was but one of a number of influences that may consciously or subconsciously have influenced Chapman. The single seater monocoque tub was a fresh application of existing technology. Costin acknowledges that the lunchtime breakthrough was Chapman original thought at its best.

Clearly, central to the concept was the method of holding the two aluminium skinned longitudinal torsion boxes - the fuel carrying tubes - rigidly in parallel. At the front Chapman set a major bulkhead assembly ahead of the driver's feet, this designed to support the suspension and steering. Then he added a diaphragm hoop to carry the instrument panel while further rigidity was added to the cockpit area by a stressed skin floor, an integral seat back and a vertical firewall. The mandatory roll hoop supplied extra bracing and behind the firewall the torsion boxes were firmly tied together by the power train. A rear bulkhead closed the end of the tub and supported the rear suspension.

The full length torsion boxes were roughly of D-section to form the lower flanks of a conventionally cigar-shaped fuselage. The nose, scuttle, cockpit surround and engine cover were all formed by detachable g.r.p. panels. The basic technology of the tub was borrowed from the aircraft industry, and this extended to aircraft-style rubberised fuel bag tanks which were tailored to fit inside the torsion boxes.

Chapman's monocoque structure was simple yet extremely effective. It weighed significantly less than an equivalent multi tubular structure and was significantly more rigid. The pioneering tub weighed 65lbs. bare, 70lbs. with mounting brackets, whereas a type 24 frame weighed 72lbs. bare rising to over 100lbs. with brackets and aluminium tanks attached. The torsional rigidity of the chassis structure was up from the 700lbs./ft. per degree of the Lotus 24 to around 1000. With the V8 powertrain bolted firmly in place that figure rose to 2400lbs./ft. per degree. The weight saving was particularly important given that the new V8 cars tended to be overweight while the big jump in torsional rigidity allowed Chapman to devise an uncompromised suspension package.

The monocoque tub was an excellent basis for producing a light, rigid car that was as slim as was practical. With the 25 the fuel was low, keeping the centre of gravity low, while Chapman could recline his driver further than ever before, the endless quest to reduce frontal area assisted by Clark's small stature it should be added. No longer did the driver have to peer over a large scuttle tank. The angle of the seat back was now a mere 35 degrees from the horizontal and the steering wheel was only one foot in diameter. The net result was a fuselage so small that the frontal area was only eight square feet - that was a staggering 11% improvement over the Lotus 18 that had won the previous year's Monaco Grand Prix.

As the 21 before it, the Lotus 25 could claim the slimmest fuselage ever seen in Grand Prix racing. With a monocoque tub less space was wasted: that was a key gain. The machine was beautifully sleek all the way from nose intake to transaxle cover. The main concern had been to keep all cowlings as tight as possible rather than to apply any complex theory of drag reduction. In general terms the cross-sectional area smoothly increased from nose to cockpit, this logical approach keeping the airflow attached. The rear of the car was also smoothly faired to form the familiar cigar shape but aft of the cockpit the air must inevitably have started to break away, spoiling the laminar flow and creating drag-causing turbulence.

Designed without reference to a wind tunnel, the Lotus 25 package was primarily functional, and it was safe. While a multi tubular chassis could be designed to protect its occupant by deforming progressively, it would have to impact at just the right angle to do that. Tubular frames tended to fold up dangerously on impact, the weakest part of the frame inevitably the cockpit opening area. The monocoque tub offered the driver greater protection upon impact with better protection for the fuel load reducing the risk of fire.

It was one thing to devise the concept, quite another to commit a major Grand Prix programme to it. As *Autosport* put it: "to break away entirely from accepted Grand Prix practice requires confidence (and ability) of the highest order".

The Lotus 25 was presented to a startled audience a mere six months or so after the original inspiration. Styman had done the detail design while few others had officially been in on the secret and news had not leaked out of Cheshunt. It had all been done behind closed doors under a production car project code number, with the recent appearance of the Lotus 24 a decoy as well as a back up should the new concept back-fire. However, Costin recalls that early on the general arrangement drawing had gone missing.

Once the project was underway Costin flew down to Portsmouth with Chapman and Styman to visit Fire Proof Tanks (FPT), well known in the aircraft world for its rubberised fuel cells. Arriving at the airport, it was discovered that the general arrangement drawing had been left behind. It never was found, its disappearance causing much consternation.

Having been drawn out again, the Lotus 25's curved outer skins were carefully panel beaten while the front and rear bulkheads were each fabricated from a number of parts as individual units. The pioneering tub was then brought together on a simple wooden jig which held the end bulkheads properly in place. The suspension pick up points were crucial and these were mainly on those bulkheads. In effect, the job was to link the two bulkheads together via metal skins. The engine mounts were accurately located via jigging plates, adjusted to fit the skin, the rest was put together as carefully as possible.

The construction was pure aircraft with brackets riveted to the skins the method of attachment for just about everything. Scammell and Woodley undertook the fabrication, learning to rivet as they went. There were headaches, of course. Scammell recalls that triangular section pipes intended to run in vee channels in the base of the monocoque proved too difficult to arrange. Then Chapman sat in the prototype tub and pronounced it too wide: 'take another one and a half inches out of it'. The bulkheads and floor had to be redone and it was then so narrow that indents had to be set into the cockpit sides to accommodate even Clark's slim hips!

Having started at the end of '61, the car was not ready before May '62. It represented around 200 man hours actual build time - not accounting for the time spent figuring solutions to the various problems that arose. The time scale was such that no running could be attempted prior to the Zandvoort appearance: the prototype was confidently wheeled out for the very first time for Clark's use in the opening Grand Prix of the season.

The car was tailored throughout to Clark who lay as far back as was feasible and changed gear virtually through rotation of the right arm. Indeed, he was initially somewhat concerned at the fact that he could not see the road close to the front of the car. He was also worried of the possible effect of the new driving position on his ability to control the machine. However, his fears would soon be allayed, once the Dutch scrutineers had accepted the radical new device...

At the heart of the untested machine (which employed much Type 24 running gear), the monocoque tub was just about a foot (304mm.) deep with no more than seven inches (178mm.) width for each of the the riveted torsion boxes. The outer skin (in other words, the curved panel) of each box was 16 s.w.g. L72 Alclad aluminium alloy sheet with 18 s.w.g. used for the inner skin throughout the length of the cockpit and also for the cockpit floor and the seat back. In the engine bay region the inner skin was 20 s.w.g. steel

*The Lotus 25 is uncloaked at Zandvoort. Note how the car is built to the cross-section of its engine, with the large fuel load kept as low as the driver rather than set high over his legs. The steering wheel was just one foot in diameter.*

while the boxes had to be halved in depth in view of the cross-sectional shape of the V8 with its splayed cylinder banks and external exhaust manifolding. The semi-stressed powertrain was effectively cantilevered and a compensating opposite-slanting internal diaphragm was fitted where the respective box sloped down to engine bay height. Ahead, the torsion boxes were kept clear internally to accommodate FPT's fuel bags alongside the driver.

The front and rear bulkheads were sheet steel fabrications to which the boxes were riveted. The front bulkhead was a five inches (127mm.) wide transverse box-like structure with a prominent flange at the rear to attach the longitudinal skins. It comprised over two dozen separate pieces and was designed to carry the inboard spring/damper units, the upper rocker arm pivots, the pick ups for the front legs of the lower wishbones, the anti roll bar, the steering rack and the pedals. The rocker arm and lower wishbone supports were set wider than the curved sides of the torsion boxes and an adjustment knob at the base of the damper also projected outside of the main fuselage cross section. In view of that the fat Armstrong knob was replaced by a clever pencil-slim control devised by Lotus.

The rear bulkhead provided gearbox and rear suspension pick ups and was formed as a simple hoop, essentially from two U-channels. The cockpit floor was angled up each side at 45 degrees while there was a corresponding bevelled lower corner to each torsion box so as to form a pair of upside down vee channels underneath the tub. Linking the engine bay to the nose, these tub belly indents accommodated water, oil, brake fluid and electrical lines. The gear linkage ran in a tube which tunnelled through the righthand torsion box from the rear bulkhead to the level of the gate. Between the firewall and the dashboard the upper inner corner of each box was also bevelled, in this case to give the driver more elbow room and the gate was outrigged just behind the dash hoop.

The dash hoop was a simple steel fabrication, the dashboard panel riveted to a tubular structure. At the rear of the cockpit the seat back and firewall were likewise riveted in place while the steel roll hoop was set above the latter. It was from this point that the torsion boxes sloped downwards and projecting from each slope was an upper front engine mount. A lower front mount was positioned directly below, these four pick up points carrying the front engine plate. At the rear the engine was bolted in via two lugs at the rear of the sump, these picking up on mounts positioned a few inches ahead of the rear bulkhead. A two inch (50.8mm) wide bellhousing forming the engine backplate linked the engine via four bolts to the ZF main case (carrying the gearbox and the final drive) while two bolts atop the main case bolted the transaxle to the top rail of the rear bulkhead. Thus, the powertrain had a total of eight tub mounting points.

As we have seen, the Climax V8 had been specifically designed to accept chassis loads while for installation reasons its front end had been kept clear of accessories. Thus, it could be kept tight to the firewall. The belt driven alternator on the righthand side charged a Varley Green Top battery that was placed immediately ahead of the dash hoop, conveniently under the driver's knees with the master switch nearby. In front of the battery, likewise on the cockpit floor was a tiny hand-held extinguisher, useful for little more than putting out unwanted cigars.

Under the driver's thighs, on the floor just behind the dash hoop were twin Bendix electric fuel pumps which fed the four twin choke Weber carburettors. Each of the three bespoke FPT fuel bags - one per torsion box, one behind the slope of the seat back - fed the pumps. The bags were fitted in through oval shaped access holes - approximately four and a half by seven inches (114mm. x 178mm.) - two cut in each torsion box inner skin, one in the seat back. The bags were clipped in place - an extremely tricky job - and the access holes were covered by plates. The three bags were interconnected, one torsion box tank linking to the seat tank while just ahead of the dash hoop a tube from the top of each box joined at a central fuel filler.

Provision was made to add to the 26 gallon (118 litre) total capacity of the regular bags with an additional six gallon (27 litre) light alloy scuttle tank, should circumstances call for it. The two and a half gallon (11 litre) oil tank was mounted in the nose, sandwiched between the front bulkhead and the combined oil and water radiator. The oil lines ran in the vee channels in the tub belly as did the return water line. The outward water line ran from a swirl pot at the front of the engine along the top of the lefthand torsion box, through a hole in the top of the front bulkhead then through a channel set into the top of the oil tank.

The oil tank was supported by lightweight rods. Ahead, the Serck combined oil and water radiator was secured by metal straps running over the oil tank, g.r.p. ducts either side of it feeding cooling air to the dampers and by the g.r.p. nose itself, which it was shaped to fit snugly. Behind the radiator and oil tank the master cylinders were packed in above the steering rack and anti roll bar, these the only items of the front suspension and controls assembly extending ahead of the front bulkhead.

The pedals were fitted with wooden foot plates in view of heat transference from the hot nose assembly. As usual twin brake master cylinders were employed, an adjustable-input balance bar linking the front and rear cylinders. The steering column took a straight run from the base of the dashboard to the rack, passing through the front bulkhead assembly. The rack was an adapted Triumph Herald item. As we have noted, rejection of modified Triumph Herald uprights in

*A further shot of the prototype Type 25 in the pits at Zandvoort. The slim line machine was built to hug Jim Clark as closely as possible and set his seat back at only 35 degrees from the horizontal. Its tub continues under the cylinder heads, as far as the rear bulkhead.*

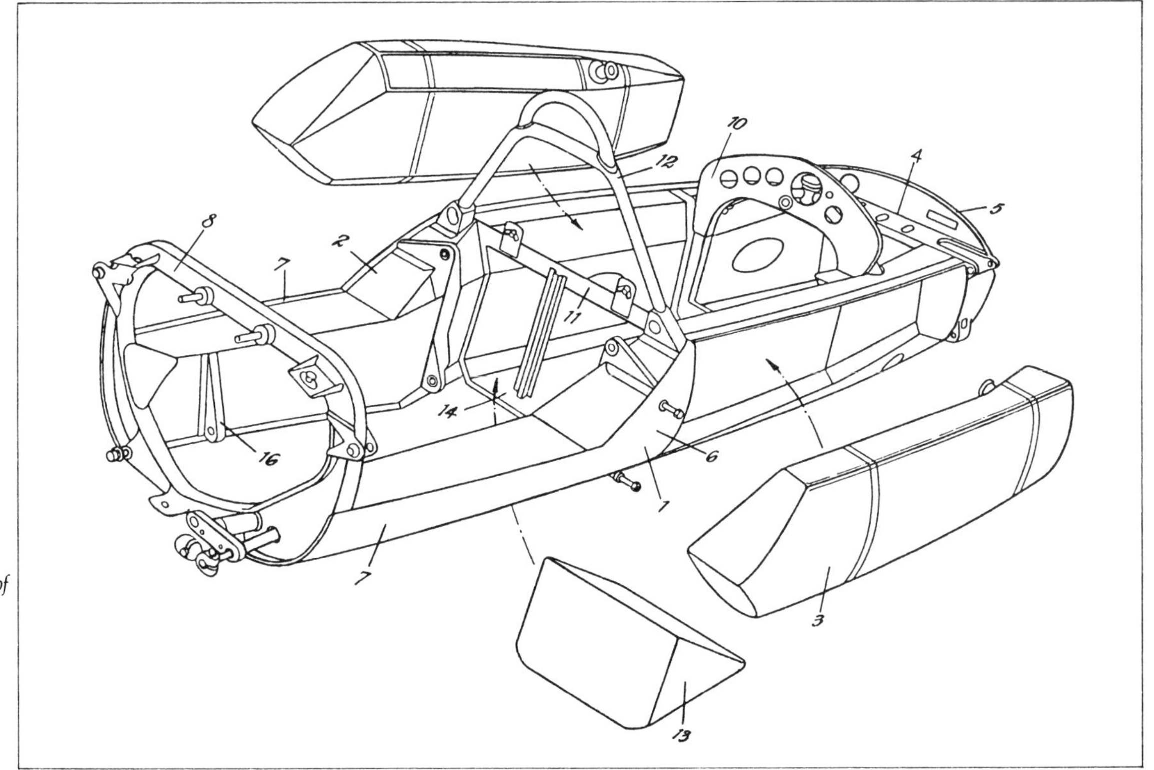


*Chapman successfully applied for a patent including this drawing and describing a chassis comprising: "a pair of spaced tubular elements of substantial width and depth . . . connected by cross members which serve to brace the structure, the engine one of the cross members".*

favour of bespoke cast electron items was a major feature of the evolution from Types 21 to 24. The Type 25 essentially adopted the suspension of the 24 with its unequal and non-parallel wishbone linkage layout.

Compared to the 21, the track dimensions of the 24 were slightly greater while the new uprights provided freedom of pick points and thus potentially improved geometry. The roll centres were a little lower, calling for the use of slightly stiffer anti roll bars while the appropriate springs tended to be slightly softer. Full anti dive had been built into an experimental Lotus 18 but though it worked - keeping the car level under braking - test driver Ireland hadn't liked it at all. The concept of anti dive had been dropped in the light of that.

With the bespoke uprights the steering track rods could be kept level with the upper wishbones to further clean the airflow through the front suspension. As we have seen, taking the spring/ dampers units out of the airstream to an inboard location offered a number of consequential advantages but clearly it did affect damper cooling, hence the air ducts either side of the radiator. Armstrong oil filled dampers were employed front and rear. These could live inboard quite happily since the fluid circulated in an ingenious 'one way' system, keeping it on the move and thus assisting heat dissipation.

At the front the bespoke upright was carried by a wide based lower wishbone and a narrow based upper wishbone, the latter the streamlined rocker arm operating the inboard spring/ damper unit. At the rear the upright was carried by a reversed lower wishbone A-arm and a single upper transverse link with twin radius rods running forward to the level of the firewall bulkhead. The rear spring/damper units were slung between the upright at the level of the lower wishbone pick up and the rear bulkhead at upper link pick up height. Conventional anti roll bars were fitted both front and rear.

The front rocker arms were chrome plated 16 s.w.g. mild steel fabrications with an internal transverse web to guard against kinking. The rocker pivoted on bearings running on a half inch (12.7mm.) diameter steel bolt which projected through the front of the bulkhead to help support the steering rack and was secured at the other end by a lock nut. Two short needle roller bearings and a central spacer were located inside the rocker while washers took up any end float. The spring/damper unit was operated through another needle roller bearing, the inner end of the rocker supporting the bolt and nut on which the bearing ran. Carrying the spring as usual, the damper embraced the rocker bearing while its lower end was secured through a simple bush.

A projection from the inner end of the rocker provided a take-off point for the front anti roll bar. The bar itself was a typical U-shaped steel rod running in twin aluminium mounts which were bolted to the front of the bulkhead. Each end of the rod was connected to its respective rocker arm extension by a short drop link with a rod end at each end. No bar adjustment was provided, alternative bars being bolted in place to alter front roll stiffness (each bar carrying its own aluminium mounts).

At the outer end of the rocker the connection to the upright was via a ball and cup joint, the bottom half cup being screwed in place to retain the upright's ball. The ball was formed at the top of a steel pin that reached far enough into the upright to pass through the steering arm. A separate lower pin completed the king pin assembly, both steel pins passing through a machined steel insert in the upright casting. The lower pin passed down through a rod end carried by the lower wishbone, adjustment at this point varying camber. Toe in adjustment was provided via the rod ends fitted to the short track rods linking the rack with the upright's forward facing steering arms. The lower wishbone consisted of a transverse link connecting to the bulkhead plus a longitudinal member reacting braking loads back into the tub wall through an unusual ball-jointed pick up.

The wishbone was a threequarter inch (19mm.) 18 s.w.g. mild steel tube fabrication and its bulkhead support was via a simple bush. The rear leg's ball and cup joint was originally designed with plates holding the cup bolted to the outer skin. However, at the build stage it was decided to provide a transverse bracing strut between the two pick up points. This steel strut ran across the cockpit floor (under the driver's shins) and extended within each torsion box to meet the

*The rear bulkhead of Type 25 chassis R1, transaxle removed exposing the clutch. The gearbox mounts to the chassis at the two points visible in the top of the bulkhead. Further back the rear engine plate mounting lugs can be seen - they are picked up by tub brackets.*

outer skin at the pick up point.

The front upright casting was star shaped, offering front and rear prongs. This allowed the same casting to be used each side with the caliper always mounted on rear prongs. The disc had an integral bell which was driven by six wheel pegs. At the front the pegs projected from a hub that ran on twin taper roller bearings carried by a fixed stub axle. This steel axle (machined internally for lightness) was an interference fit in the upright which it ran right through, secured at its inner end by a circlip. A castellated nut kept the tapered hub on its shaft while the wheel was bolted on via the hub's six drive pegs and in turn held the disc in place.

The rear suspension's single transverse upper link was connected to the upright and to the rear bulkhead via simple bushed joints. The lower A-arm was picked up by the rear bulkhead through a rod end, adjustment here varying camber. Rod ends were also carried by the A-arm to pick up the base of the upright. The spring /damper unit and lower radius arm also connected to the base of the upright while the upper radius rod picked up at driveshaft level, opposite the caliper. The radius rods' bushed tub pick ups consisted of brackets riveted to the outer skin. Again 18 s.w.g. mild steel tube was employed for the linkages while the steel rear anti roll bar ran between mounts outrigged from the inboard damper pivots and was connected via drop links to the outboard end of the A-arm.

The rear uprights were machine-handed. Each carried a live rear stub axle via sealed roller bearings running on its shoulders. The Hooke-type outer driveshaft u.j.'s steel cast yoke was splined to the axle while the two upright shoulder bearings were separated by a spacer. An outer axle flange carried the six drive pegs as an interference fit and again the wheel held the disc in place.

Front and rear, the 10.5" (267mm.) diameter, plain cast iron Girling discs were stopped by Ferodo DS11 pads in single two pot 'AR' model calipers. No form of brake cooling was supplied and the brakes were set within Lotus' own magnesium rims. These were disc wheels of the 'wobbly web' pattern - lighter and stronger than wire spoke wheels. Lotus and Vanwall had pioneered these wheels in 1958 and by '61 only

Ferrari clung to the traditional wire type. The Lotus 25 drove and secured each wheel via six studs since centre lock fixing was not considered worthwhile, tyre changes no longer a feature of races.

The familiar Dunlop R5 tyres were carried on 15" (381mm.) diameter rims front and rear, though some rival constructors favoured 13" diameter fronts. D9 and D12 (green spot synthetic tread) tyres were still the regular wear, the front tyre for the 15" rim being the 500-15 R5 P (Prototype) model, a wider treaded version of the 500-15 R5 seen in '61. It was carried on a six inch (152mm.) wide rim and had a section width of 7.12", a tread width of 4.22" and an overall diameter of 25.06". The 650-15 R5 rear tyre was carried on a seven inch (178mm.) wide rim and had an overall diameter of 28" and a tread width of 4.7".

Power was supplied to the rear wheels from a regular AP twin plate 7¼" gear driven clutch which drove through the Lotus' usual 5DS10 ZF syncromesh gearbox. The input shaft ran back under the final drive to a two-shaft gear cluster, the upper shaft feeding forward to the c.w.p. The case was magnesium and had detachable top cover (this originally its sump), rear cover, endplate and sideplates. The detachable sideplates accessed the final drive while the gear cluster came out through the rear cover.

It was not feasible, however, to change even c.w.p. ratios at the track and thus spare 'boxes offering different c.w.p. ratios were carried for each car. The five intermediate ratios could not be changed at all. The gear linkage was very complex and included a so called 'interlock' mechanism to ensure that the driver could only select an adjacent ratio. Effectively the interlock consisted of a plate set directly under the gate with trip levers worked by the gear lever to open the correct path.

The c.w.p. carried a conventional ZF l.s.d, as first employed in Grand Prix racing by the V16 Auto Union of the mid Thirties. Drive out from the transaxle was via Metalastik rubber 'doughnuts', as first employed on the Lotus 21. The doughnut ring was hexagonal providing three input and three output points equally spaced. Its flexible rubber construction cushioned the transaxle from road shocks while allowing for the inevitable slight variations in driveline length with suspension movement. The popular alternative was to employ splined slip joints but there was a danger of the splines binding up under heavy power load, this 'stiction' inhibiting suspension movement. The driveshafts were hollow steel and fed Hardy Spicer 1300 series Hooke-type joints.

Twin chromed tail pipes ran over the gearbox, emerging from the 'spaghetti' pipe cluster above the bellhousing. Of necessity, the individual cylinder pipes hugged the heads very closely and a heat shield was placed between the pipes and the rear of the engine. The engine and transaxle were completely shrouded, only the tail pipes and intake trumpets emerging from the fuselage cowl. A gauze cover allowed the carburettors to breathe, in the interest of fuel cooling. The nose, scuttle and cockpit fairings were in one piece, with separate engine and transaxle shrouds for ease of access, all the fuselage cowling in g.r.p. The advanced use of g.r.p. rather than traditional lightweight alloy panels was hardly surprising given that Lotus produced a g.r.p. chassis car, the Elite.

The curved tub flanks were exposed to the airstream while the g.r.p. upper fuselage was quickly-detachable. The front fairing slipped over the radiator and three pins along the top of each torsion box and was secured via two Dzus fasteners at the rear of the cockpit. Carefully streamlined and part-enveloping the cockpit opening, the windscreen was perspex, and bullet-shaped rear view mirrors were attached directly to it. The engine shroud hugged the FWMV and was connected to the front fairing via two Dzus fasteners, and was held at the rear via two springs. The transaxle cowl was in turn fixed to the rear bulkhead via four Dzus fasteners.

The spark box was mounted behind the trumpets, in the open air. The only fuselage air scoop was the small nose aperture. As noted, the air intake was divided between the radiator and the dampers. The radiator air exited through the bottom of the fuselage, which was open between the radiator and the front bulkhead. The damper cooling air was able to filter into the cockpit where it hopefully cooled the pedals and the driver. The driver of R1 was, of course, Jim Clark, who took his place on Friday May 18, ready for the first run...

*ʼhe revolutionary ıonocoque on its simple ɔooden jig. The ɔngitudinal aluminium ɔrsion boxes were riveted ɔ the front and rear ulkheads which were re-assembled steel abrications. The engine ıounts are clearly visible n this rear-on view taken n September '62 of tub ʻ5.*

*The Chapman ıonocoque tub had a omplex front bulkhead, roduced from over two lozen components. The kins were riveted to a lange on the rear of it, as s evident from the double ow of rivets immediately ɔehind the bulkhead. ⁼ront suspension mounts ıold bulkhead to jig.*

*Overleaf: details of the Lotus 25 exposed in the actory in September 1962. The car remained essentially unchanged hroughout the '62 season, its advanced specification right from he word go. Indeed, modifications for the '63 season were few and of a detailed nature.*

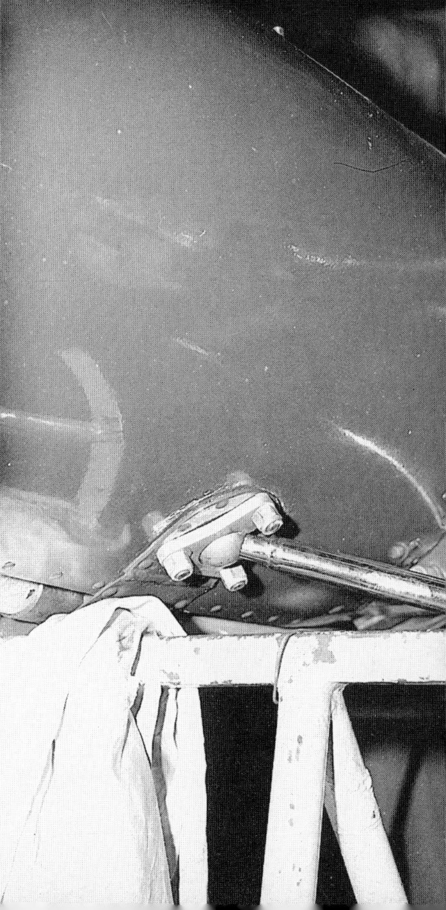

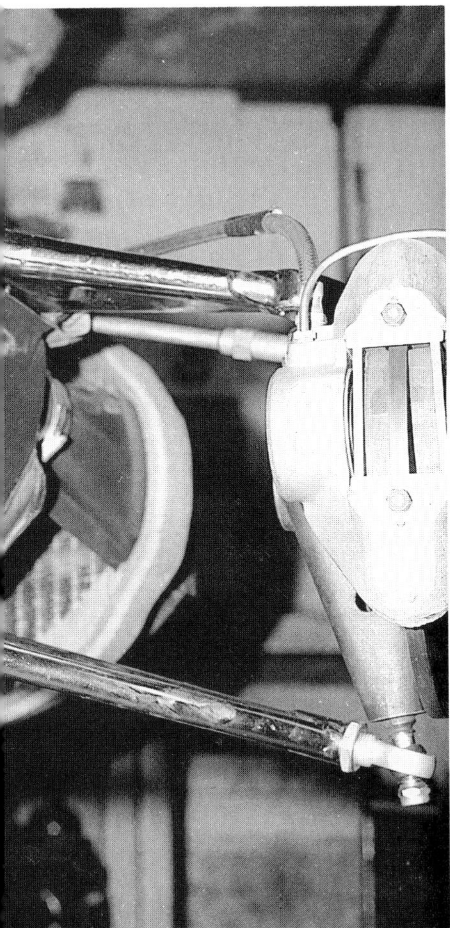

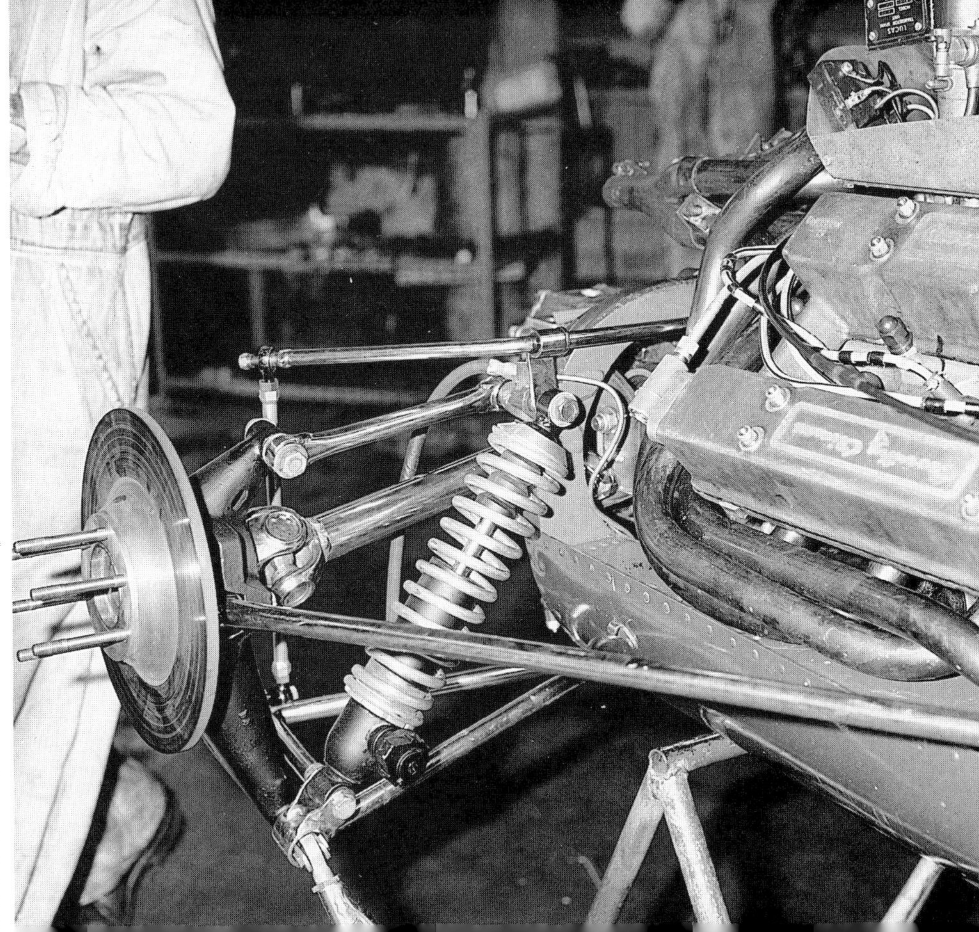

# DIARY

**Zandvoort (NL) May 20**
*Dutch Grand Prix*
*Clark.... Q: 3/R:9*

Lotus 25 chassis R1 literally startled the motor racing world as it rolled out into the Zandvoort paddock: the secret had been well kept. It didn't roll right onto pole position though, Clark suffering engine and gearbox headaches and winding up 0.7 second adrift of Surtees' new Lola which pipped the fuel injected BRM V8 of Hill. Pole position, however, counted for little on race day: his engine having been flown back to Coventry for a rebuild, Clark cut across from the outside of the front row to lead into the first corner. Within two laps the Scot had built a two second lead over Hill's BRM leading the pursuit.

Alas, just as it looked as though Clark had the field covered - this including the works teams from Lola/Bowmaker, BRM, Ferrari, Cooper and Porsche - his clutch started slipping due to fault at the pedal. The BRM cut the gap: at the end of lap 11 Hill was right on Clark's tail. Exiting Tarzan the Lotus slowed, Hill was through and the dream debut was over. Clark limped back to the pits and sportingly rejoined after long repairs to the pedal assembly, to finish ten laps in arrears.

**Monte Carlo (MC) June 3**
*Monaco Grand Prix*
*Clark.... Q: 1/R:NR*

Practice witnessed a battle of Hill and Clark and R1 came out on top by four tenths of a second, after the BRM had held pole for much of the final session. The start of the race was chaotic as Willi Mairesse made an over ambitious attempt to win the first corner from the second row. Slow starting, Clark was clouted by the charging Ferrari and he emerged from a first corner melee in sixth place. Troubled by his clutch, he took almost a quarter of the race to cut through the pack. Then, the clutch working properly, he could set about Hill who had pulled a seven second lead.

Lap record after lap record brought Clark to within one second of the BRM. Then better breaks in traffic helped put Hill over seven seconds ahead again as the race reached half distance. Clark had started to feel clutch problems once more. Soon the Lotus was stranded with an inoperative clutch and an engine malady. Arch rival Hill didn't make it two in a row, however, stopping with a broken engine and victory went to McLaren's Cooper.

**Mallory Park (GB) June 11**
*2000 Guineas*
*Clark.... Q: 1/R:NR*

In the absence of BRM, Ferrari, Porsche and Cooper, Clark won pole by a comfortable margin but Surtees' Lola won the start and led all the way. Clark made a poor start, soon found low oil pressure and retired rather than lose the engine just after half distance.

**Spa Francorchamps (B) June 17**
*Belgian Grand Prix*
*Clark.... Q: 12/R:1*

Lotus still had only one 25 chassis but there were now V8s for all the major British factory cars. Ferrari replied with four V6s while Porsche was a regretted absentee. Clark had a serious engine failure in the first practice when a dowel in the camshaft drive failed and a replacement engine, sent by road, arrived too late for a run in the second and final session the following day. Although not even in the qualifying top ten, by the end of the first eight mile lap of the majestic road circuit Clark was fourth. There were then five cars in contention and Taylor's works Type 24 led at the completion of the second lap, chased by McLaren, Mairesse, Hill and Clark all in a slipstreaming bunch.

Clark was content to run fifth as the others swapped position, playing himself in, making up for lost practice time. After ten of 32 laps he was ready to make his mark and with a succession of fastest laps he asserted himself at the front, a comfortable 10 seconds ahead at half distance. Hill had meanwhile suffered a sick engine and McLaren subsequently lost his engine. Fighting for second place then were Taylor and Mairesse: Taylor's car jumped out of gear, Mairesse ran into it and both crashed heavily, thankfully without driver injury. Clark went on to win at a canter from Hill's spluttering BRM.

**Rheims (F) July 1**
*Rheims Grand Prix*
*Clark.... Q: 1/R:NR*

Ferrari and Porsche were absent from this non-championship event but all the other major factory teams were in attendance. Although Clark annexed pole - some seven seconds under the '61 Ferrari record - Surtees made a better start and held a clear advantage when the 25 split its swirl pot on lap 5. The water gushed out and that was that. McLaren was the eventual winner, the Lola failing.

**Rouen (F) July 8**
*French Grand Prix*
*Clark.... Q: 1/R:NR*
*Taylor... Q: 12/R:8*

At last Lotus produced a second Type 25 - logically R2 - allowing Taylor to take over R1. Due to a manufacturing fault outside of Lotus the steering rack jammed on the new chassis, giving Clark a hairy moment. Nevertheless, he set the pole time in the car, 0.2 second faster than Hill's BRM. Porsche was back but surprisingly the French Grand Prix was lacking Ferrari representation, industrial action at the factory taking the blame.

On race day Clark made a poor start and trailed Hill and Surtees, unhappy with the steering on R2. Surtees hit trouble and Hill tangled with a backmarker handing Clark the lead but the BRM soon overcame its setback. Clark then stopped at the pits, his steering seriously amiss. The top left wishbone/upright joint had pulled apart and the car was withdrawn. Hill later fell out of the running with fuel injection problems and Gurney was the surprise winner for Porsche.

• Diary continues on page 56

ırt of the French
ʳand Prix at Rouen
th Clark on pole in
2, 0.2 second faster
ın Hill's BRM, 0.6
ond faster than
ʼcLaren's Climax-
ooper. Alas, a front
spension joint pulled
t and Clark saw
urney's third row
rsche (just visible)
me through to win.

# The Correct Combination

Right from the outset, with no testing the combination of Clark, Lotus 25 and Climax FWMV was a potential winner. Of course, it had not been a forgone conclusion that Clark would race the 25 straight out of the box at Zandvoort, logically he tried both it and a proven 24 in practice. In spite of inevitable teething troubles, the 25 was the only way to go. Clark had a clear edge over the opposition at Zandvoort only to hit trouble early on, and looked to have the measure of Hill at Monaco before unreliability dashed his hopes. A margin of superiority was once again evident at Francorchamps and this time it resulted in a well deserved win. Further convincing wins followed at Aintree, at Oulton Park (in the Gold Cup) and at Watkins Glen.

Alas, the list of further lost opportunities in Europe reads: Rouen, Solitude, the Nurburgring. Only on the ultra-high-speed Rheims and Monza circuits did rivals appear to have the potential to beat Jim Clark in a straight fight. At Rouen, Rheims and Monza Clark's car failed him as it had done at Zandvoort and Monaco, while at Solitude a wrong mixture setting cost competitiveness and driver error cost a finish. Clark made few mistakes but on this occasion he was caught out by the onset of rain. At the 'Ring misted goggles saw him forget to switch on his

# • Diary continued

Running in mid field, Taylor had suffered a sticking throttle and took over the engine cover from R2, having left his own by the trackside following makeshift throttle repairs. R1 finished six laps behind in eighth place. Crossing the line flat out, the unfortunate Taylor could not avoid tangling with another car in a needless accident triggered by muddled action on the part of the police controlling the finish. That post-race shunt left R1 a write off, its tub damaged throughout its length, while Taylor was again badly shaken but uninjured.

**Solitude (D) July 15**
*Solitude Grand Prix*
*Clark.... Q:* 1/R:NR
This race should have been a walk-over from pole for R2 with only Porsche to present a serious challenge. However, Gurney led from start to finish in his flat eight car. Clark found he had the wrong mixture setting, then he spun off following the onset of rain, caught out by the sudden change of conditions.

**Aintree (GB) July 21**
*British Grand Prix*
*Clark.... Q:1/R:1*
Ferrari was back, but with only a single car for reigning Champion Phil Hill who could not find competitive speed against a full complement of factory teams. In contrast, it was an almost perfect weekend for Clark. Surtees, second on the grid, was 0.6 second slower, Graham Hill a full second slower and the 25 ran away with the race while Surtees gave vain chase. Fastest lap went Clark's way too. The only imperfection: the gearbox got hot in the last few laps, forcing Clark to ease off.

**Nurburgring (D) August 5**
*German Grand Prix*
*Clark.... Q: 3/R:4*
Gurney found early speed from the under-powered Porsche on the company's regular test track and pole on Friday was protected by rain the following day. Ferrari was back to four cars but Bandini crashed the long awaited prototype '62 chassis. Another novelty was the first Brabham chassis. Race day was wet keeping Gurney well in contention, together with Hill's BRM and Surtees' Lola.

Clark would have been there, too, but he had been so busy trying to de-mist his goggles that he had forgotten to switch on his electric fuel pumps. Having consequently started dead last he passed a remarkable 17 cars on the first lap and by lap eight of 15 he was up to fourth and gaining on the leading trio. However, intermittent fuel starvation then helped take the edge off his somewhat imprudent speed. Hill won from Surtees and Gurney, all three splashing home within five seconds with Clark just over half a minute adrift.

**Roskildering (DK) August 26**
*Danish (non championship) Grand Prix*
*Taylor... Q: 8/R:6*
*(Aggregate result)*
*Heat 1* 10
*Heat 2* 5
*Heat 3* 5
An unsuccessful outing for Taylor in R2. This unusual and poorly supported three-heat affair was dominated by Brabham's customer Type 24-Climax.

**Oulton Park (GB) September 1**
*Gold Cup*
*Clark.... Q: 2/R:1*
*Taylor... Q: 10/R:NR*
With the August lull Lotus had been able to build up its third Type 25 chassis and Taylor unexpectedly drove R3 after his 24 struck an engine malady. Although the foreign works teams stayed away there was a strong entry from the UK and Ginther's works BRM posted a practice time that Clark was able to equal, not to better in R2. However, from the middle of the front row Clark ran away from everyone. Hill rather than Ginther led the rest home while Taylor, 'running in' the new chassis had found trouble early on, a radius rod pick up pulling out of the monocoque.

**Monza (I) September 16**
*Italian Grand Prix*
*Clark.... Q: 1/R:NR*
*Taylor... Q: 16/R:NR*
Now running R3 Clark suffered a gearbox failure, Taylor a rear suspension fault on Friday, then Clark's new gearbox seized warming up for Saturday's practice. It was fixed only for the engine to play up so Taylor handed his car over and waited for R3 to be fixed. The engine was repaired only for the gearbox to lock up! The upshot was that Clark was on pole, just three hundredths of a second faster than Hill's BRM while Taylor languished well back on the grid (which featured all the major marques).

Clark made an excellent start but was quickly overtaken by Hill. On the third lap Clark - unable to respond to the BRM - pitted with a seizing transmission. He restarted a lap down only to retire while Taylor likewise suffered yet another broken gearbox. Hill went on to collect his third '62 World Championship race win ahead of Ginther.

**Watkins Glen (USA) October 7**
*US Grand Prix*
*Clark.... Q: 1/R:1*
*Taylor... Q: 8/R:12*
Clark took pole without undue effort and through the early stages edged away from Hill. However, he tripped up passing tailenders, giving Hill a break. Hill's lead was shortlived, Clark setting a new lap record as he reasserted his authority. Hill finished nine seconds behind, after Clark had eased up with clutch trouble. There was no one else on the same lap. Taylor finished 15 laps down after gear linkage then oil pressure trouble.

Ferrari had pulled out for the rest of the year and now Porsche quit Formula One altogether. Clark had now equalled Hill's three World Championship wins and a fourth win at the East London finale would make him Champion, irrespective of Hill's finishing position. However, he trailed by six (corrected) points so the advantage

• Diary continues on page 58

fuel pumps, almost certainly at the cost of victory.

After transmission trouble at Monza, that win at Watkins Glen was the start of a Type 25 hat trick, Clark taking over Taylor's car in Mexico following a black flag for a push start. At Westmead - the penultimate event Team Lotus contested in '62 - Clark was hampered by fuel vaporisation on an experimental injection engine but Taylor won. Thus Team Lotus went into the all important World Championship decider on the crest of a winning wave.

In terms of speed Clark deserved to have been Champion Driver and in the eyes of some he had already assumed the mantle of Moss and Fangio. For example, in *Motor Sport* Denis Jenkinson spoke of, "his effortless high speed driving... he is a worthy replacement for Moss on any circuit, although he cannot yet match Moss' experience".

Hill, of course, had more Formula One experience than his new sparring partner. Clark's relative lack of experience makes his overall '62 performance all the more impressive. Further, Costin notes that Clark almost always drove with a margin of safety, though if it was really necessary he could 'hang it all out'. Typically, he took pole position in relaxed fashion, to the carefully concealed dismay of his opponents. In his Aintree report, having witnessed yet another Clark pole Jenkinson remarked: "It is uncanny the way he seems to say 'I will now set a new fastest lap' and goes out and does just that, and the works Lotus is seldom 100% in all respects. One day it will be spot-on to everyone's satisfaction and then Jimmy Clark will do a really fast lap!"

Of course, as the experienced Moss knew the hard way, motor racing is about finishing first rather than being the quickest on the track and on that basis Hill, in notching up four wins was a worthy title holder. The points system tended, rightly or wrongly to reward consistency and Hill finished all nine rounds, only once outside the points and only three times off the rostrum. By way of comparison Clark ended up with only

*Side-by-side passing the start/finish line stands, Clark in the V8 Lotus 25 and Mairesse in the '61 Ferrari V6. Mairesse is sitting upright in the '61 Championship winning car, Clark is fully reclined. Once in front, there was no keeping up with the laid back Scot.*

# • Diary continued

was to Hill while Lotus now had three points less than BRM in the Constructors' Cup. Again, one more victory would tip the scales its way...

**Mexico City (MX) November 4**
*Mexican (non championship) Grand Prix*
*Clark.... Q: 1/R:NR*
*Taylor... Q: 3/R:1*

This race was shunned by BRM while Surtees had shunted his Lola at Watkins Glen and borrowed Brabham's Lotus 24 only to suffer ignition trouble. Lotus 24 customer cars hadn't often shone through the season and Brabham was now fully committed to the new BT3 which he had shipped out to Mexico. He finished runner up to Clark who won in spite of taking over Taylor's car (R2) after his pole sitting car (R3) had been black flagged for a push start. It was a great come back drive by Clark.

**Kyalami (ZA) December 15**
*Rand Grand Prix*
*Clark.... Q: 1/R:1*
*Taylor... Q: 2/R:2*

The World Championship finale was the culmination of the South African 'Springbok' series of three races. Only Lotus and BRM of the factory teams ran all three races. This first round saw Clark (R3) and Taylor (R2) ahead of Hill on the grid and first and second in the race, Clark leading all the way while the BRM team suffered ignition (Hill) and gearbox failure. Surtees ran this race with an older Lola but could not catch the Lotus duo.

**Westmead (ZA) December 22**
*Natal Grand Prix*
*Clark.... Q: 1/R:2*
*Taylor... Q: 3/R:1*
*Heat result:*
*Clark.... 12*
*Taylor... 1*

Here chassis R4 made its debut carrying an experimental fuel injected Climax engine, Taylor retaining R2 with R3 as spare. The Westmead field comprised Lotus and BRM plus a host of local entrants (only two with V8s) and was split into two heats. Clark led the first from pole only to suffer fuel vaporisation, a setback which put him on the back of the grid for the final. Taylor won the second heat, beating pole man Hill who met ignition trouble. Taylor then won the final in R2 while Clark came through to take the runner up spot in R4 in spite of a high speed misfire.

**East London (ZA) December 29**
**South African Grand Prix**
*Clark.... Q: 1/R:NR*
*Taylor... Q: 9/R:NR*

For the World Championship finale R4 became the spare car as Team Lotus phased in another new chassis, R5, for Clark with a regular Climax engine. Chassis R4 was still equipped with the prototype injected V8 and measures had been taken to try to cure the misfire. In addition to Lotus and BRM, the Lola/Bowmaker, Cooper and Brabham works teams supported this event, Cooper racing McLaren's car with an injection engine. Nevertheless, only two drivers were in contention: Clark and Hill, the new Lotus taking pole by 0.3 second. No other driver was within a second of this pair.

Clark had switched between carburettor and injection cars in practice, the latter posting a lap 0.4 second faster than the race car with its proven engine. On this occasion Clark made a superb start and he headed Hill by a second at the end of the first lap. He continued pulling out a second a lap for the first dozen laps, then eased off a little. Hill was unable to respond.

While Taylor retired from mid field with a broken gearbox Clark sailed on towards victory, pulling out almost half a minute by half distance in the 200 mile race. Lap 61 of 82 saw the first sign of trouble: blue smoke poured from the rear of the Lotus. In the words of *Motor Sport*: "For two laps Clark maintained his speed but on his 64th lap he pulled into the pits as the oil pressure had been surging in the corners on this lap. Colin Chapman and Jim Endruweit looked in all the obvious places for the oil leak and it was some time before they found the small hole in the crankcase hidden behind the heat shields between the exhaust pipe and the back of the engine.

"At first they didn't know what was missing from the hole but, when checking with the spare engine, they found it was a bolt approximately two inches long which located the jack shaft bearing that had fallen out and was letting the oil spray out onto the exhaust. Further investigation showed that on the spare engine the locking washer had left a firm impression in the alloy crankcase whereas on Clark's engine there was no such impression. This proved at least to the Lotus mechanics that no such locking washer had ever been fitted".

four World Championship race finishes: three wins plus a fourth place.

Clark's points-robbing retirements were twice transmission related, twice chassis related, once engine related. Although Climax found itself in an unwelcome spotlight thanks to that lost last chance at East London, the fact is that Lotus pedal bracket failure had cost the likelihood of victory at Zandvoort, upright joint failure an equal chance at Rouen and either of those nine point scores would have been enough...

Taylor effectively enjoyed only half a season in a 25, contesting only four World Championship races in the model and adding nothing to Lotus' Manufacturers Cup score from those starts. Perhaps as a legacy of the massive, telegraph pole demolishing Spa shunt, he invariably qualified in mid grid thereafter. Of course, just two races after Francorchamps he crashed very heavily for a second time, wrecking the prototype 25. In the 25 Taylor later retired twice due to transmission failure, while he finished both his other races in the car eighth after various setbacks. However, prior to his shunts he had been second at Zandvoort in a Type 24, that result giving Lotus a final Cup score of 36 (whereas Clark scored 30 points) against 42 for BRM.

The obvious skill of Clark makes it difficult to judge the merit of the 25 chassis. Clearly it was every bit as good as the best of the rest - arguably the 24 - but was it inherently superior, or would Clark's skill have carried a Type 24 ahead of the pack? Certainly the 25 had the right ingredients in its low weight, low centre of gravity, minimal frontal area and excellent chassis engineering. It did appear that the pioneering stiff monocoque tub basis allowed it to make more of its suspension and thus of its tyres.

In general, thanks to its chassis rigidity and scientific suspension the Lotus 25 could run softer springs than rival cars, to the particular benefit of slow corner performance and tyre life. Clark - ever driving smoothly - used one set of D12s for three races, plus practice periods. This season the D12 was regularly run in the dry on slow and medium speed circuits with the D9 reserved for high speed work. By this stage Dunlop had a lot more knowledge of the synthetic tread, and had gained more confidence in its use. Thus, the D9 was employed only at Spa Francorchamps, Rheims and Monza, the D12 regular wear elsewhere.

The soft springing of the Lotus 25 ensured its tyres stayed in constant contact with the track. Dunlop had a saying; 'a wheel in the air gathers no cornering force', and Chapman had taken it to heart. That much was evident right from the outset, Jenkinson remarking of first practice at Zandvoort: "the new 25 was riding the bumps beautifully..."

In contrast, World Champion Hill liked his car particularly stiffly sprung, with stiff springs and roll bars and high tyre inflation pressures. Typically, Clark might run pressures of 32 - 34p.s.i. front - rear, Hill of 40 - 44p.s.i. Tyre pressure was one of the key ingredients of car set up and the Type 25 had its rolls bars and springs changed only occasionally at the track. There was no bar adjustment at the front and bar swapping was a lengthy job since it involved removing the radiator, oil tank, dampers and rockers. Generally a ½" thick bar was run but alternatives of 9/16" and 5/8" were available, increased bar thickness promoting understeer.

Those who worked with him say that Clark was never ultra-critical of his car's set up. He could report accurately how the car was working but did not constantly fiddle with settings, unlike Hill. Clark's natural flair could accommodate any problems posed by the set up (while Hill's fiddling was apt to lose him direction).

Regardless of Clark's skill, it is clear that with the patent-applied-for monocoque chassis, Lotus was ahead of the pack when it came to making the most of the R5 equipment on offer in 1962. The 25 had excellent camber control and could be precisely tuned to a circuit. Indeed, Vic Barlow noted that the 25 was the most finely and delicately balanced of the '62 crop. Chapman generously put the success of his car down to the tyre but it is evident that the significant factor was that the Lotus 25 was allowing the tyre to do its job properly. The innovative Lotus 25 unlocked the full potential of the ever improving Formula One rubber emerging from Fort Dunlop.

Aerodynamically, there is no evidence to suggest that the Lotus 25 was superior to its rivals. Indeed, at Rheims, on the Paris-Soissons road both the Type 25 and the Lola were timed at

168m.p.h., with the BRM next up at 165m.p.h. Significantly, perhaps, as we have already noted Clark lost his edge at Rheims and Monza. These were the two circuits where top speed was of paramount concern.

With the 25 essentially right straight out of the box there was little chassis modification over the season. Both Lotus works cars raced without gearbox cowls at Francorchamps since high gearbox temperatures had been registered in practice. Tail shedding subsequently became a regular occurrence. Extra tankage was required at Francorchamps and Monza, the latter calling for the full 32 gallons to last the long 307 mile/500 kilometre event.

Chassis R2 debuted at Rouen on experimental 13" front rims but soon switched back to regular 15" rims. The 13" rim was run with a 5.5" section height hence the tyre was one inch lower in overall diameter. Dunlop preferred the larger tyre option since it offered a lower running temperature. On the other hand, a smaller wheel assembly reduced unsprung weight and rotational inertia as well as aerodynamic drag, and lowered the role centre and the centre of gravity. However, all these gains were marginal and the Lotus suspension had been designed specifically to suit 15" rims which allowed bigger discs while the bigger tyre offered a slightly larger contact patch.

The later chassis - in total five were constructed in '62 - employed thinner aluminium skins in the tub, saving unnecessary weight. During the course of the season the rear bulkhead was beefed up, while the lower radius arm's monocoque pick up had to be strengthened following the debut of R3 at Oulton Park. This car's tub had quickly lost its left side pick up bracket, the bracket heavily loaded since the lower radius arm took braking forces. The bracket had been simply riveted to the outer skin and subsequently a strengthening plate was added internally.

Other notable chassis failures were seen in the Zandvoort, Rheims and Rouen races. At Zandvoort a bolt came loose in the clutch pedal bracketry, the pedal took up clearance in the master cylinder and consequently the clutch slipped. At Rheims the swirl pot split, while at Rouen the front left upright's upper ball joint came loose on Clark's new car and the throttle

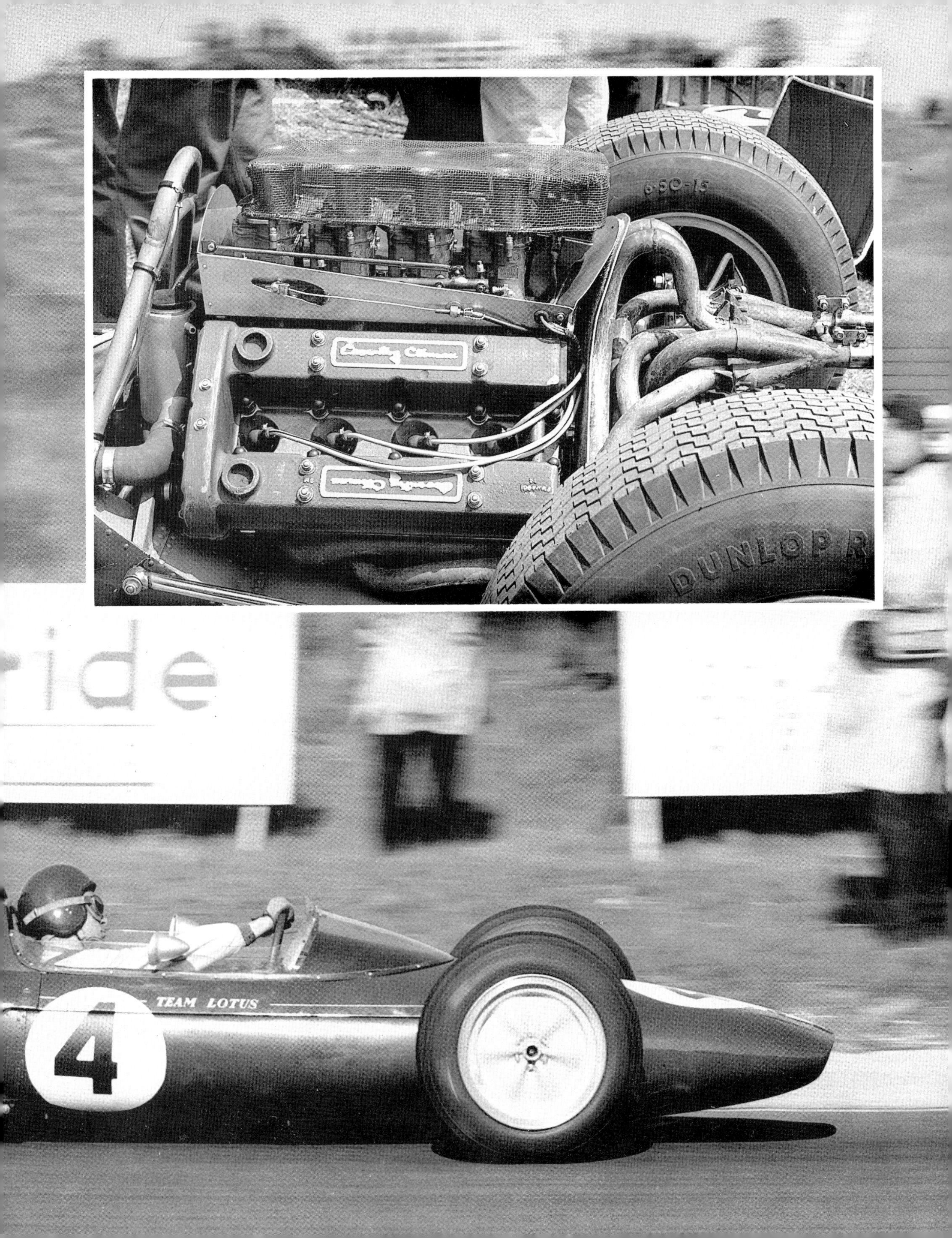
6·50-15
DUNLOP R
ride
TEAM LOTUS
4

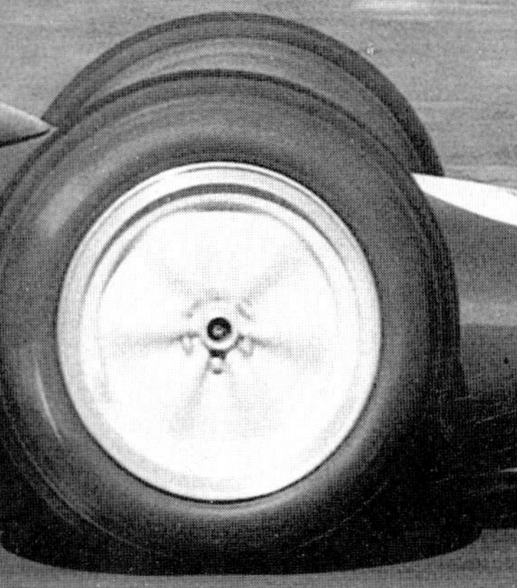

linkage got snagged on Taylor's car. The steering rack practice failure for the new chassis was echoed by Brabham's Type 24 and was traced to over-hardening of the teeth on the rack.

Transmission troubles were rife this season, generally the complex gearbox linkage to blame. In the opinion of those who worked on it, the ZF linkage was not really up to its job. At Monza there was a spate of actual gearbox failures, but this was later traced to the lubricant. A new double-strength molybdenum disulphide additive was so effective that certain roller races became over-lubricated and consequently revolved in their housings.

The ZF interlock system was not well liked by the drivers. Clark had developed a technique for fooling it, a certain amount of fiddling with its under-the-gate levers allowing him to go straight down from fifth to second when necessary.

After the problems of the prototype Climax V8 engines, the 'Mark II' '62 production version was commendably trouble-free. However, at Francorchamps Clark had a serious engine failure in the first practice when a dowel in the camshaft drive failed. Then there was the East London oil loss...

Climax settled on the use of 21-4NS for both inlet and exhaust valves, seating respectively on hydural bronze and austenitic steel. Hassan told the S.A.E. that, "21-4NS becomes workhardened with use and provided a very favourable seat condition together with almost complete absence of valve failure".

This season Mexico City was a new challenge in terms of set up due to its high altitude, thin air demanding a mixture 10-12% weaker. The only engine development problem experienced by Lotus through the season was a spate of early tappet failures. In his autobiography Hassan says, "it was some time before we discovered that Lotus' Esso racing lubricants were different from those we normally used, and from those used by other customers. To kill the problem we eventually resorted to using some of Baron Beck's excellent Molyslip compound, which we buffed into the tappets very thoroughly to provide a

*The quickest runner the 1962 Wo Championship Drivers was Lotus pilot Jimmy Cla previous page. The Lo 25 (seen at Zandvoo was propelled b regular customer vers of the Coventry Clim FWMV V8 eng (inset) equipped w four Weber carburetto*

*Jim Clark in Lotus 2 R2 at the 'Ring, flank by Chapman (left) an Crew Chief Endruwe (right). Contrast t sleek lines of the Clima V8 propelled monocoq machine with those the Cooper in which t FWMV was launch at the 'Ring one yea earlier (page 19).*

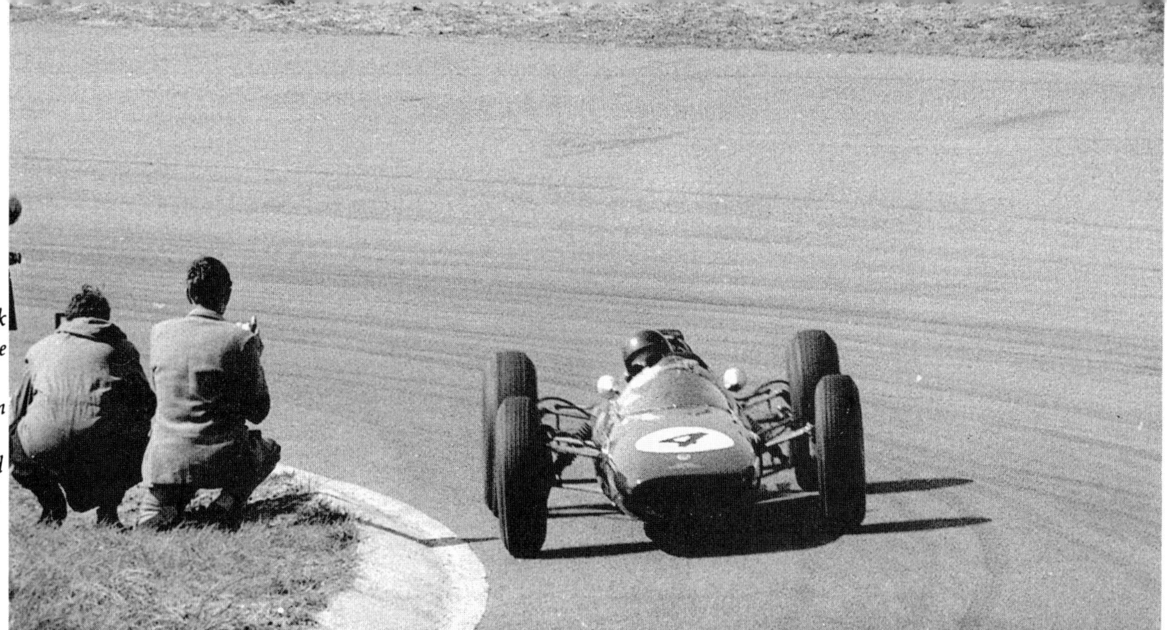

artist at work: Clark st time out in the Type at Zandvoort. Car mber four rolled out in nt of an astonished lience in Holland and radical configuration ved the ideal trument for the ented Scotsman. gether Clark and us 25 spelled success.

## From the Cockpit

The December 28 1962 issue of *Autosport* recorded a conversation between journalist David Phipps and Jim Clark in which Clark gave the following insight into driving the Lotus 25.

DP: What would you say is your line around a circuit, by comparison with the average line?
JC: Nowadays I think I probably go into corners earlier than I used to.
DP: Less of a sweep you mean?
JC: Yes, less of a sweep - in fact, trying to shorten the distance round the circuit. I also find that I am going further into the corner under braking - starting to turn in with the brakes on.
DP: Which is why you sometimes begin to lock up the inside front wheel?
JC: Yes, because I'm still braking hard as I'm turning into the corner. Sometimes, if I find that I am not going quickly enough, instead of braking later I try to get off the brakes earlier, which means I go into the corner quicker.
DP: What is your ideal car? Do you like a car to understeer, or oversteer?
JC: ...As far as Formula One is concerned a slight tendency to understeer is probably a good thing, because understeer can be corrected without losing too much time, whereas correcting oversteer is liable to waste time.
DP: And power.
JC: Yes. And there's another thing. You can make an understeering car oversteer but you can't make an oversteering car understeer - at least I can't.
DP: Do you worry about getting the Lotus 25 out of shape?
JC: Not so much as in the 18, or even the 24; in fact, it feels to drift more than any of them. I don't mind the tail coming out in a corner, as long as I've got enough arm movement to deal with it.
DP: How much do you have to alter your Lotus technique when you drive a car like the Aston Martin?
JC: Oh, it's completely different. At Goodwood this year it took me the whole of the first practice seeing to get back into the groove of driving an Aston. At first I was trying to drive it round corners like a Lotus!
DP: Instead of throwing it around, and using the power to promote roadholding?
JC: Oh, you do that to a certain extent on the Lotus as well. You know, it gives you a better bite through a corner if you can get on the throttle.
DP: Does the tail of the 25 come out much if you lift off in a corner?
JC: No, not very much. It all depends on the attitude you're in. If you're understeering, obviously it won't come out very much, but if you're right on the limit then it will. I use this technique to promote oversteer on an understeering car when I want it.

## CHASSIS LOG

R1

New for Clark at Zandvoort. For Clark at Monte Carlo, Mallory Park, Spa Francorchamps and Rheims. For Taylor at Rouen. Written off at Rouen.

R2

New for Clark at Rouen. For Clark at Solitude, Aintree and Nurburgring. For Taylor at Roskildering. For Clark at Oulton Park. For Taylor at Monza, Watkins Glen, Mexico City, Kyalami, Westmead and East London.

R3

New for Taylor at Oulton Park. For Clark at Monza, Watkins Glen, Mexico City and Kyalami. T car at Westmead.

R4

New for Clark at Westmead. T car at East London.

R5

New for Clark at East London.

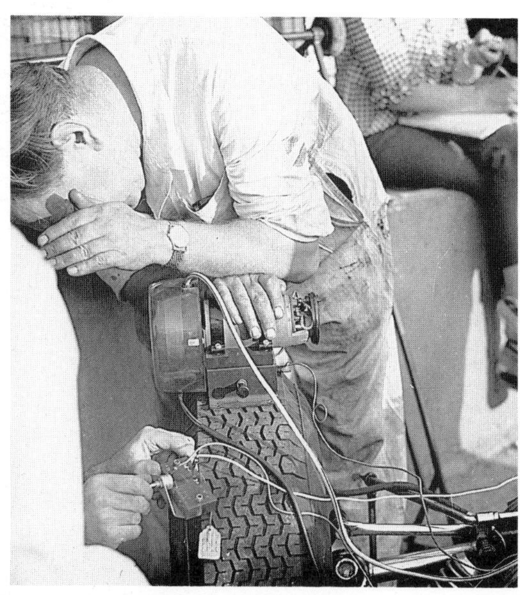

satisfactory surface treatment".

In general, Climax appeared to have its strongest relationship with Jack Brabham. In his autobiography Hassan opinions: "the interesting point about Clark was that, although he was a supreme driver... he was not sensitive enough in the engineering sense to tell us much about the behaviour of our engines. He built up a remarkable relationship with Colin Chapman, and could describe very precisely his thoughts on the driveability of the car itself, but he seemed unable to tell us much about the operational characteristics of our engines. This contrasted very strongly with Jack Brabham who was an excellent mechanic as well as a world-class driver, and could be relied upon to give us a full report".

Although running to only 8,500r.p.m., the Mark II FWMV clearly gave Clark all the power he needed to do the job. While his title bid was made using Weber carburettors throughout, South Africa found chassis R4 equipped with that prototype fuel injected FWMV, this using the indirect Lucas system as pioneered by BRM. Driveability rather than power gains were sought. The basis of Clark's injected engine was the first ever FWMV, the one debuted by Brabham at the 'Ring in '61.

The Lucas metering unit was fed by a high pressure Lucas pump which in turn was fed by the usual twin Bendix pumps. The new equipment was fitted beside the gearbox, in the open with an aluminium shield to keep powertrain heat away. High speed misfire bugged the engine and for East London a third Bendix fuel pump was added to try to cure it. That wasn't the solution and the mechanics found themselves bleeding the system every few laps. In desperation they re-routed the fuel lines and asked Clark to watch for air bubbles at top speed! Clark set a best time 0.3 second faster in R4 but opted to race R5 with its dependable Weber engine.

All five 25 chassis carried Climax V8 engines and ZF gearboxes but there was some experimentation with the BRM V8 and Colotti 'boxes on the Team's 24s. At Monaco Lotus's 24 T-car appeared with a the Bourne V8 and a six speed Colotti while for Rheims Taylor had a new 24-Climax with a five speed Colotti. Still Team Lotus was evaluating the BRM-engined 24 and it

*An unusual view of Lotus 25 chassis R1 in the paddock at Rheims, July 1 1962. More efficient packaging was a major monocoque gain. The car no longer carries a transaxle cowl, high gearbox temperatures having been recorded two weeks earlier at Spa Francorchamps.*

was at last raced, as a third entry, by Arundell who suffered a broken fuel line. It subsequently went to Ecurie Filipinetti.

The Colotti gearbox was the creation of Valerio Colotti, designer of the Maserati 250F's transmission and running gear. Based in Modena, Colotti ran his 'Gears Speed Developments' concern in conjunction with Rob Walker's Chief Mechanic Alf Francis. Colotti offered a Type 32 five speeder and a new Type 34 six speeder designed specifically for the new British V8 engines and only 559mm. long.

This season ZF, Colotti, Jack Knight / Cooper, BRM, Ferrari, Porsche and Hewland / Brabham all produced Formula One gearboxes and Colotti, Cooper, Ferrari and Porsche all felt six speed developments to be worthwhile in the face of increasing engine speeds and narrow power bands. Cooper ran the FWMV with a six speed 'box from the outset. However, there was no attempt to run the FWMV-Type 25 with a six speed gearbox. The eventual World Champion ran his high r.p.m. V8 on a five speed 'box, BRM trying the lightweight six speed Colotti early on but staying with its own overweight but dependable unit. Apparently the vibration of the BRM V8 was unkind to the transaxle.

By Spa Francorchamps, round three of the World Championship, all the serious runners had six (Ferrari) or eight (Climax, BRM, Porsche) cylinder engines. While the FWMV could not be taken over 8,500r.p.m., the Ferrari and Porsche engines could reach five figures while BRM ran to 10,500r.p.m. Had BRM enjoyed the same level of power per 1000r.p.m. as Climax it would have had a 25b.h.p. advantage but the best figure recorded at Bourne in '62 was 190b.h.p. That followed the introduction of revised pistons, in time for Monza.

BRM played with both stack pipes and low level blended pipes but couldn't fit a crossover system and thus its pipe blending - and its power curve - was unavoidably compromised. However, like the Climax V8, the BRM V8 was commendably dependable in its first full season.

While BRM successfully exploited the Lucas injection system throughout the year, Ferrari failed to race ready its experimental injected engine prior to its post-Monza withdrawal. Ferrari still claimed 200b.h.p. but it lacked acceleration compared to its new British rivals, its power band clearly too narrow. Porsche simply lacked power thanks to its traditional 'boxer' configuration and (unwilling to switch to a conventional V8) this prompted its withdrawal from Grand Prix racing. Gurney's successes had flattered the uniquely torsion bar suspended, air cooled German car.

*Seeking the source of the spill. Chapman (right) and Endruweit will find the origin of the oil leaking onto the East London pit lane in a missing bolt at the rear of the Climax FWMV. Meanwhile, lost lubricant having cost his title chance, Clark has vacated the cockpit of R5 . . .*

63

# The Beach to the Brickyard

With the East London finale held on December 29 the '62 season all but ran into 1963 and for Team Lotus the new year was a continuation of the old with the same drivers and the same cars. However, the technical staff had changed during the course of '62, Mike Costin having gone to join partner Keith Duckworth in the growing Cosworth company on a full time basis. Returning to Lotus, Len Terry was now responsible for racing car development.

This year engine rather than chassis developments were the centre of technical interest and all were relieved to be continuing the successful Lotus-Climax partnership following a threatened withdrawal by the Coventry company. In October '62 Lee had announced the end of his company's involvement in racing with the end of the year, "as racing is no longer economic". That statement emphasised the fact that Climax was spending a lot more on racing than it was getting back from competition sales and service. Its prices did not reflect the true cost of its involvement and the enhancement of company prestige could only go so far in offsetting the deficit. Further, the non profit making racing work was tying up a lot of key engineers.

Lee could not be blamed for his decision and the constructors hardest hit - in particular Lotus and Cooper - set about finding means to support the continued involvement of the private engineering concern. Here the support of the fuel and tyre companies was, once again, vital. In late December Lee was able to make the following announcement:

"Following my statement on October 17th that my company intended to stop the manufacture and development of Formula One racing engines, I was invited to discuss this decision with some of the leading members of the British motor industry. At this meeting it was emphasised what great importance they attach to Grand Prix racing as a testing ground for new motor engineering developments.

"It was proposed that the motor industry would increase its financial support to a limited number of Formula One racing car constructors so that they, in turn, could contribute at least in part to our development expenses. Recognising the importance of the facts presented to me for the reconsideration of our decision, we have agreed to produce a limited number of Grand Prix engines next year. These will incorporate lessons we have learned during the present season..."

Thus, Hassan was able to conclude his work on injection, and phase in a new short stroke configuration. Six new engines were built for '63, and in addition eight of the existing 16 customer units were converted to Mark III specification. Two of the new units went to Lotus, two to Cooper, one each to Brabham and Reg Parnell (Racing), the latter taking over the Lola project following the withdrawal of Bowmaker. There were however, to be no further 1.5 litre Formula One Lola models.

Existing engines were converted to Mark III specification for a charge of £3000 while new engines were sold for £5000, Climax' prices still not fully reflecting its costs. In March the company was taken over by local firm Jaguar Cars, Lee remaining as Managing Director. Happily, Jaguar was keen for Climax to continue its high

*The Coventry Climax injected V8 trailed the injected BRM V8 by a season. BRM pioneered the innovative Lucas shuttle metering system, taking it to a World title in 1962. Climax jumped on the bandwagon a year later and for the first time had straightforward fuelling.*

profile involvement in Grand Prix racing.

Aside from Grand Prix racing, Lotus now had a contract to contest the Indy 500 with a derivative of the 25 chassis. Gurney had been tremendously impressed by the monocoque when it rolled out at Zandvoort and had straightaway persuaded Chapman onto a plane bound for Indiana, to witness the 500 race that same month. Gurney was driving a mid engined car produced by Mickey Thompson and propelled by a General Motors engine and he had his eye on Ford's increasing involvement in racing. In due course a contract had been signed with Ford whereby Lotus would field Ford engined cars for Clark and Gurney in the '63 500 mile race.

After the '62 United States Grand Prix Lotus had taken its cars to the Brickyard, where the 25 ran laps of 142/143m.p.h. On that basis Ford calculated that a winning combination would be the 25 chassis plus a 350lb. engine producing one b.h.p. per lb. A pushrod aluminium V8 from the Ford Fairline was seen to foot the bill and the Detroit giant's engine development department rolled into action. Meanwhile, at Cheshunt Lazenby was assigned the Indy project, for which the 25 chassis design had been suitably redrawn. Derek Wilde then joined the Formula One race team.

Although Lotus continued to produce cars for the lesser formulae, there were no further Formula One customer machines. In the Grand Prix arena Gurney was still a major rival for Clark, joining the Brabham team following the withdrawal of Porsche. Hill and Ginther continued to comprise the BRM line up, McLaren and Maggs the Cooper representation. Surtees switched from Lola to Ferrari while Phil Hill moved to ATS, the team formed by Ferrari deserters.

# Higher Aspirations

The potential of the Lotus 25 had been obvious in '62 and for 1963 Chapman had nothing to add to his successful formula. Chassis R2, R3, R4 and R5 were all in existence, R4 and R5 only one race old and this equipment was carried forward essentially unchanged. The only significant developments for the new season were the fuel injected short stroke Climax engine and a new Dunlop tyre. The injected engine called for a one inch (25mm.) longer wheelbase while more subtle chassis modifications included improved bearings for the front wishbone inboard pivots and the radius rod chassis pick ups, a modified oil system, a lighter radiator and modified nose air ducting.

During '62 larger diameter - 28mm. - oil pipes from the engine to the nose mounted tank had been called for and these sizes side by side would not fit comfortably into a belly vee channel. Chapman had therefore put a 20mm. pipe within a 40mm. pipe to flow the oil each way, a very neat solution. Now the tank was redesigned with an integral swirl pot system to enable it to run with less oil and less air space above. The slimming process saved over 12lb., mainly by weight of oil and the far smaller tank was sculptured so as to present a vee shaped bow to the air exiting the radiator.

The damper inlets flanking the radiator were removed, replaced by NACA-type intakes set into the sides of the nose. Air collection for the dampers had been robbing the radiator of air. The radiator was slimmed from ten to six rows saving a further 15lb. These chassis modifications were applied to both carburettor and injected cars.

Whereas in South Africa the prototype injected car had accommodated the Lucas metering unit alongside the gearbox it now sat in the valley of the engine as originally intended, driven by a toothed rubber belt from the half speed jackshaft. The pulley could only be accommodated on the jackshaft by moving the water pump forwards. This called for a revised front engine plate which added one inch to the length of the unit. In effect, the powertrain was pushed back by one inch and rather than angle the driveshafts forwards the wheelbase was extended by a matching amount.

The rearward shift of the engine and transaxle called for spacers at the chassis pick up points while the rear suspension had modified pick ups and longer radius arms to move the rear uprights back the required amount. The lower A-arm's inboard pick up was the most tricky to modify. Instead of the A-arm's rod end bolting straight into the rear bulkhead it had to be rotated through 90 degrees to be clamped into a new bracket extending from the bulkhead. On the righthand side the new bracket ran under a gear linkage support, consequently the bolt securing the rod end could not be lock-nut secured and it was wired instead.

The injected engine's metering unit was fed by a Lucas high pressure electric pump which in turn was supplied by the usual twin Bendix fuel pump system. The high pressure feed suppressed vapour formation, ensuring metering accuracy in spite of the heat faced by the metering unit thanks to its location within the vee. The high pressure pump was a black cylindrical object known as 'the bomb' which had to be kept cool and remained on the gearbox. The new position for the metering unit displaced the oil filter and this was moved to a gearbox bracket while the spark box was moved to a cooler location on the lefthand side of the roll hoop.

Whereas BRM had found great success with the Lucas injected system, for Climax it had only worked when the injector nozzles were mounted atop the intake pipe, right in the centre of its orifice. For '63 the system was encouraged to work with a more satisfactory lower injector positioning, just upstream of the throttle. Short nylon pipes linked the injectors to the metering unit which was supplied fuel at the constant pressure of 100lb.sq.in. by the bomb.

The fully-mechanical metering cum mixture control unit responded to both engine load (throttle opening) and engine speed. It was of the shuttle type, containing a free floating - "shuttling" - piston. The throttle slides were linked by a finely

*For 1963 Lotus redesigned its oil system with a more advanced nose tank incorporating a swirl pot. The traditional tank needed to carry more oil with plenty of air space above. Lotus' new tank could carry less, saving weight, and was far smaller as is evident here.*

adjustable rod to a carefully contoured cam which in turn controlled exactly how far the shuttle could move. That distance, varying with throttle opening, determined precisely the amount of fuel fed to each injector. The cylinder in which the shuttle operated rotated at engine speed uncovering ports through which the measured and now timed spurt of fuel was dispatched to each injector.

The injector was of the spring loaded poppet valve type and under the influence of fuel pressure sprung open to produce a fine spray in the inlet port. The low mass of the shuttle provided very rapid response to engine acceleration or deceleration and for this V8 version of the Lucas system a twin bored rotor was employed. The system was capable of producing up to 1,200 injections per second of metered fuel.

Lucas' injection system was developed in conjunction with the short stroke configuration FWMV. In itself, the injection system did not give higher power but it did produce sharper response. Hassan noted that, "it made it possible to achieve really clean acceleration out of a bend and was a most worthwhile modification". Meanwhile, the short stroke configuration allowed higher revs and thus higher power. The so called Mark III '63 injected engine had a bore and stroke of 67.94 x 51.56mm, a stroke:bore ratio of 0.76.

The shorter stroke reduced piston acceleration at a given r.p.m: higher speed could be run for a comparable stress level in terms of piston acceleration. To further assist, the con rod centre distance was lengthened from 4.2 to 5.1in. (129.5mm.), the rod:stroke ratio rising from 1.78:1 to 2.5:1. The net result was a maximum acceleration of 100,300ft.sec.$^2$ for a 67.94mm./2.675in. diameter piston running at 9,600r.p.m.

Total piston area was up from 38 to 44 sq.in. Climax did not, however, take advantage of the potential of the bigger bore for larger valves. Peak power speed went up from 8,500 to 9,600r.p.m. and officially the Mark III engine produced 195b.h.p. at that speed on a compression ratio of 11.0:1. Maximum torque was 118lb.in. - as the earlier engine - at 8,000 rather than 7,500r.p.m. Hassan documented that, "there were some small changes to the inlet system which gave minor improvements. The inlet port was enlarged from 1.015 to 1.025in. diameter and was provided with a 20 degree included taper entry which reduced the effective length of the restricted diameter by approximately one inch. The diameter of the large end of this tapered entry was 1.312in. and this increase was extended to the throttle body diameter and ram pipe".

A 195b.h.p. Mark III engine could be produced via a conversion kit, including the injection package, a short stroke crank, revised rods, pistons, liners and so forth. Lotus acquired two Mark III engines.

The new footwear for '63 was Dunlop's so called R6 tyre which had been designed specifically to exploit the D12 compound even on high speed circuits. The move to an all-purpose synthetic tyre was another impressive step by the Birmingham, England based company and was accompanied by a wider tread, 0.4" wider at the front, 0.5" wider at the rear and appropriately widened casing. Lotus still ran on 15" rims having 6.0" front, 7.0" rear rim widths (Chapman typically favouring use of a rim slightly larger than that for which the tyre had been designed).

The R6 maintained the overall diameter of the R5 while the aspect ratio was slightly lower, 65% - 68% according to the rim width employed. With the extra tread width the contact patch was around 5% greater while the wider section offered greater lateral stability and with less distortion the tread stayed on the track better. However, the move to the universal use of green spot rubber was more significant.

With the lower aspect ratio Dunlop was able to slightly reduce the tread thickness at the shoulder, helping minimise the temperature problem. Further, the bias angle of the plies was slightly reduced since lowering the bias angle was known to tend to reduce heat build up at high speed. The lower bias angle packed the cords more tightly for a stiffer carcase. It also pulled the tread down slightly, so there was more on the road. This was the first constructional change since the introduction of the nylon carcase R5 and along with it came a modified tread pattern designed for improved water clearance.

*The colour photograp on the next eight pag show Clark's Clima Lotus in action durin 1963. The photograp show – in order – Cla at Monte Carlo in th locations: under t railway bridge, in Casi square and chasing H through Station hairpi then Clark at Mexi City and Zandvoo Surtees' Ferrari alongside on the Mexic front row and can also seen chasing Clark a the BRMs of H (leading) and Ginth (third) through t Monte Carlo railw bridge into Portier corn which leads onto t seafro*

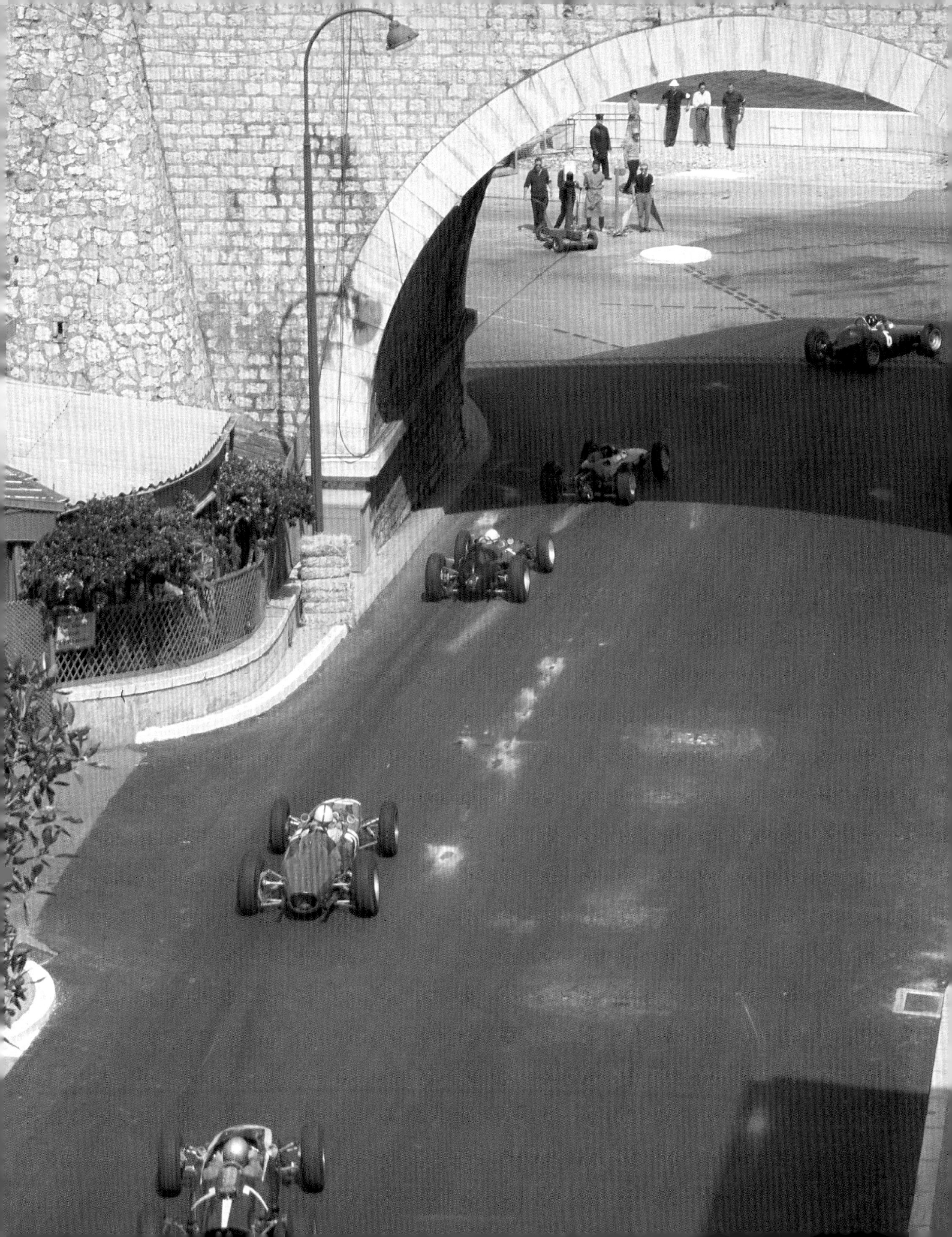

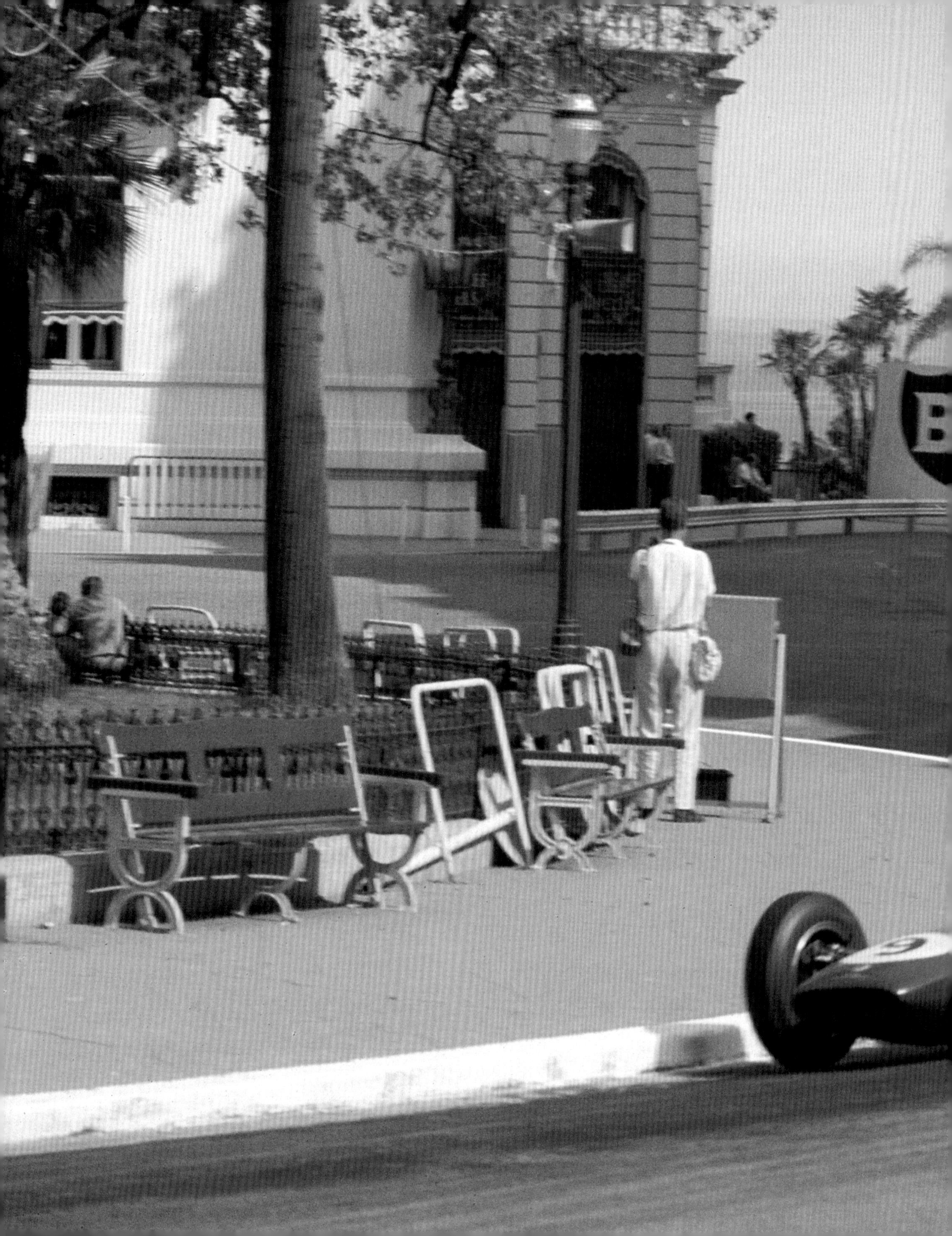

9

EXPEDITIONS

2 MINUTE
8
TEAM LOTUS

6
SO

# Escape Act

In the hands of Jimmy Clark, the Mark III Climax-engined Lotus 25 could typically draw steadily away from its opposition, and usually it survived to win. The only times when others could keep the flying green machine in sight came at the Nurburgring, where a sick engine plus an awkward gear change was too much of a handicap even for Clark, and at Monza. Only at Monza, where above all top speed counted and slipstreaming was so great a factor did rival cars find the measure of the Lotus. Nevertheless, Clark won. Clark was virtually unbeatable in 1963 Grands Prix. Retiring once (at Monaco) and suffering a sick car twice (at the 'Ring and at the start of the Watkins Glen race) he won a remarkable seven of the ten World Championship events, usually from pole. It was a record number of victories in one season and that achievement was backed by the highest points total ever.

Writing in *Autosport* after seeing Clark's handling of the FWMC-25 at Monte Carlo, John Bolster made the following observation:

"The combination of Jimmy Clark's phenomenal skill with the characteristics of the monocoque Lotus resulted in some extremely fast cornering. For example, at Mirabeau Jimmy was visibly faster than anybody else. He not only entered the corner at very high speed, but he seemed able to kill an incipient skid with a mere flick of the wheel.

"The drivers of other cars tended to leave their line and lose speed under similar circumstances but the Clark-Lotus combination was never off the chosen path. The car is very light and the driver is small, while the chassis is exceptionally rigid. It is understood that the Lotus has not yet been developed to its limit as far as roadholding is concerned, but it must already have a useful advantage in this department, though again I would stress the skill of Clark."

Of course, Monte Carlo was the first venue to host Clark's escape act and here his ZF gearbox failed and spoiled it, possibly due to over-caution on the part of the Scotsman. In *Motor Sport* Denis Jenkinson explained:

"Being so far in front Clark had begun to ease his pace and instead of flicking the gear lever from one notch to another he had begun to ease it gently... the selector and spring loaded plunger movements in the ZF gearbox are very small and rely on a certain amount of their own inertia in order to engage properly. By flicking the gear lever briskly this is achieved, but easing it gently from one notch to the next did not impart the necessary inertia to ensure full engagement and on the fateful gear change on the harbour front the selector had sprung back the wrong way".

Monaco was the only non-points scoring race for Clark: his seven wins were backed by one second and one third place, the pickings from the Nurburgring and the Glen respectively. Aside from the gearbox failure at Monaco and gear linkage trouble at the 'Ring the only parts that proved faulty during World Championship races were a plug and a fuel pump.

All in all it was a truly remarkable season that established Clark as one of motor racing's All Time Greats and Lotus as a thoroughbred marque. Coventry Climax had already known championship success with Cooper but had now succeeded against stronger odds, beating BRM, Ferrari and ATS in a real engine war.

On the flip side, Chapman was somewhat distracted by the Indianapolis bid in 1963, the second Lotus 25 did not share the reliability of the lead car and on occasion the Team fell apart in practice, as it had done in '62. *Motor Sport* had dubbed it "Team Shambles" at Monza in '62 and allotted it the same tag during practice at Spa Francorchamps this year. Nevertheless, Clark

# DIARY

**Snetterton (GB) March 30**
*Lombank Trophy*
*Clark.... Q: 1/R:2*
Team Lotus rolled out a familiar chassis for the first 1963 Formula One race: R3, Clark's USGP winning machine. It was equipped with a familiar long stroke Weber-equipped Climax V8 for the Scotsman, the team's sole runner. He faced two '62-style works BRMs, as usual for Hill and Ginther with a revised flat plane crankshaft V8 for the former. Hill missed practice and thus started from the back of the grid while Ginther got the jump on Clark at the start.

Clark didn't take long to assume the lead on the damp, slippery track but Ginther came back at him and re-took the lead while Hill was slicing through the field. Hill gradually hauled in the Lotus and both passed Ginther, Hill going on to win, "looking so determined yet so relaxed, whereas Clark looked the opposite, probably due to being out of practice, not having raced since last year", according to *Motor Sport* reporter Denis Jenkinson.

**Pau (F) April 15**
*Pau Grand Prix*
*Clark.... Q: 1/R:1*
*Taylor... Q: 3/R:2*
Here Taylor had the Snetterton car, Clark R5 which was equipped with the new short stroke, fuel injected Climax V8. There was no factory opposition but Bonnier in an ex-works '62 V8 Cooper run by Rob Walker split Taylor from Clark on the grid. Clark was over two and a half seconds faster than Bonnier while Taylor had suffered a troubled practice. Come race day and there was no challenge to Team Lotus' total domination, Clark cruising home playing cat and mouse with Taylor.

**Imola (I) April 21**
*Imola Grand Prix*
*Clark.... Q: 1/R:1*
*Taylor... Q: 2/R:9*
This weekend Taylor out-qualified Bonnier, though he was still over two seconds slower than Clark's Mark III Climax-engined R5. On race day, R3 suffered a gear selection problem and Taylor finished 14 laps down after lengthy pits attention. Clark cruised home unaccompanied while Taylor set the lap record without the use of fourth gear.

**Aintree (GB) April 27**
*Aintree 200*
*Taylor... Q: 5/R:3*
*Clark.... Q: 1/R:7*
For the first time short stroke, injected Climax faced the revised flat plane crankshaft BRM engine. Cooper (McLaren and Maggs) and Brabham (Brabham) also had the Mark III Climax. Brabham, however, holed a piston in practice and was forced to withdraw. Clark was in full command of qualifying but found himself with a duff battery at the start, losing one and a half laps. Then R5 was not running strongly so just after one third distance he took over Taylor's fifth placed Weber-equipped, long stroke V8 machine. In spite of losing half a minute or so during this operation, Clark managed to work R3 up to a remarkable third place ahead of Ginther and McLaren, Hill winning from an inspired Ireland in a BRP entered Lotus 24-BRM.

**Silverstone (GB) May 11**
*International Trophy*
*Clark.... Q: 6/R:1*
*Taylor... Q: 5/R:3*

Ferrari at last joined in the fray, sending two new-style (still spaceframe) chassis for Surtees and Mairesse propelled by Bosch injected versions of the familiar 120 degree V6. Lotus, BRM, Cooper and Brabham were again out in force while Ireland was again on cracking form and he took a surprise pole. The regular brace of 25s was off the four-strong front row, Clark suffering engine and suspension bothers.

On race day, however, Clark was soon out front in R5, harried by McLaren - ahead for the first three laps - then Surtees. Approaching quarter distance Clark started to pull away. Meanwhile, Ireland had spun and World Champion Hill's BRM had fallen sick. Then Surtees' car failed leaving Climax V8s first, second and third, though Taylor was somewhat lucky to share the rostrum with Clark and McLaren, Ireland making a strong recovery and finishing right in his wheeltracks.

**Monte Carlo (MC) May 26**
*Monaco Grand Prix*
*Clark.... Q: 1/R:8-NR*
*Taylor... Q: 9/R:6*
*Brabham.. Q:15/R:9*

Lotus sent a second Mark III engined car - R4 - for Clark and R5 for Taylor while opposition again came from all this year's major factory teams: BRM, Cooper, Brabham and Ferrari. In Thursday's opening practice session Clark improved on his '62 pole time by 0.1 second and also set second fastest time in the Mark II-engined R3 spare. He went a second faster on Friday and was content to conduct full tank tests on Saturday. Hill wound up 0.7 second slower while Ginther shared the second row with Surtees. Meanwhile there had been a lot of trouble among the other Mark III Climax users, the upshot of which was that Brabham lost his ride. Lotus responded with the loan of R3 which Brabham started from the back of the grid.

Hill and Ginther outdragged Clark at the start and it took Clark five laps to get into second place, there to start hounding Hill. BRM acceleration was a problem and having eventually got ahead Clark went wide at the Station hairpin and dropped back to third! It was not until 20 laps had run that the Lotus was able to stamp its authority on the race though the margin of superiority was not that great, the lead at 50 laps - half distance - a useful 8.5 second gap.

Hill, however, had met his match and Clark was able to ease off over the latter

• Diary continues on page 84

*: 1963 World ampionship opened at nte Carlo where nding title holder l led Clark in the y stages. Here Clark nds the flat-crank ipped BRM with its roved exhaust ing: BRM leration was a blem. However, once ad the Lotus was cker.*

won the Belgian Grand Prix, and convincingly so.

While Clark had a near perfect season, Taylor had a dreadful time. Failing to find sparkle again for Lotus after his '62 accidents, this season's big shunts at Francorchamps and Enna Pergusa were a further horrendous shakings, amazing escapes of the wrong kind. Taylor could not be blamed for either. The huge accident at Francorchamps was caused by the bolt securing the lower right rear A-arm falling out. This was the bolt which had to be wired since a lock nut could not be fitted in the available space. It appears that the safety wire had been left off. R5 smashed into a marshal's post at Stavelot and its tub split in half.

One point scored earlier by Taylor at Monaco was the sum total of the World Championship score for the second Lotus, which was also driven by Arundell and Spence. The Indianaplois adventure was another disappointment, Clark losing a possible win after leader Parnelli Jones laid an oil slick in the late stages. Indianapolis was run just a short while after Monaco and throughout the balance of the season Clark was on a roll. World Champion Graham Hill had a new flat plane crankshaft BRM engine with a wider power band but it simply wasn't enough. Clark made everyone else an also ran.

Although the flat plane crankshaft version of the FWMV made its entrance at Francorchamps in a new Rob Walker Cooper and attracted much attention, Clark did not try one before Zeltweg. There was no performance gain and Clark did not race one in the remaining World Championship events. The engine's advantage was one of

# • Diary continued

part of the race. Alas, the gearbox seized. Clark's wheels locked solid: Hill - shrugging off a challenge from Surtees - was handed victory. Neither Taylor nor Brabham had featured, Brabham finishing 23 laps back after suffering gear selection problems while Taylor had pitted suspecting a similar malady but had been able to run home two laps down.

**Spa Francorchamps (B) June 9**
*Belgian Grand Prix*
*Clark.... Q: 8/R:1*
*Taylor... Q: 11/R:NR*
Clark quickly ran into more gearbox trouble as practice got underway in Belgium, then Taylor comprehensively wrecked R5 after the rear righthand lower A-arm's inboard retention bolt fell out at high speed. Clark suffered another bout of transmission trouble in the second day's qualifying and only just scraped into the top ten while badly shaken (and finding it difficult to move) Taylor courageously started the R3 spare from mid grid.

Clark made a demon start from his lowly position to lead into the first corner and soon he had only Hill for company. On a track wet in places Hill steadily fell away. Again the race rightfully belonged to Clark and this time around it was Hill's gearbox which failed. McLaren uplapped himself during a late race storm and the Cooper was the only other car on the same lap as the touring Lotus. Taylor had handed his card in early on.

**Zandvoort (NL) June 23**
*Dutch Grand Prix*
*Clark.... Q: 1/R:1*
*Taylor... Q: 10/R:10*
R2 replaced R5 for Taylor, fitted with a Mark III Climax and a new Type 35 Colotti six-speeder: finishing touches were put to it in the paddock. BRM had a new monocoque style chassis but it wasn't race-ready. Clark tried the Colotti six speed 'box then set a convincing pole time in R4. And on Sunday he simply motored away from everyone. Taylor started from mid field once again and stopped early to investigate a misfire. Suffering a fuel feed problem, he wound up 14 laps behind his remarkable team leader.

**Rheims (F) June 30**
*French Grand Prix*
*Clark.... Q: 1/R:1*
*Taylor... Q:7/R:13-NR*
*Arundell. Q:15/DNS*
Here in champagne country R4 was again comfortably on pole. It was once more backed by R2 for Taylor and R3, which Peter Arundell practised but did not start since FIA regulations forbade him to enter two races and the organisers wanted him as a star of the Formula Junior event. Only Hill - racing the new BRM - got anywhere near Clark in practice (0.7 second adrift) and the race was a Clark demonstration from start to finish, in spite of a wrong mixture setting costing some high r.p.m. performance. Although R4 was off form the opposition literally fell apart! Taylor typically started from mid field and ran into trouble - but not before he had won the temporary glory of second spot. He suffered a flat battery then retired with driveshaft failure.

**Silverstone (GB) July 20**
*British Grand Prix*
*Clark.... Q: 1/R:1*
*Taylor... Q:10/R:NR*
Once again Clark had the measure of the field in R4, taking pole 0.2 second clear of Gurney's Brabham, 0.4 second clear of Hill back in the spaceframe BRM. Jack Brabham led at the end of the first lap with Clark fifth. Lap two and Clark was third behind Brabham and Gurney, lap four and he was in front. Already Taylor's mid field progress in R2 was hampered by fuel pump trouble. Clark led the rest of the race with ease while Taylor was stopped by a combination of fuel pump and transmission trouble.

Five Grands Prix had now been run and Clark had won four of them in a row: one more win from the remaining five rounds would give him the maximum possible 45 point World Championship score.

**Solitude (D) July 28**
*Solitude Grand Prix*
*Clark.... Q: 1/R:NR*
*Taylor... Q: 5/R:NR*
*Arundell. Q: 4/R:2*
Lotus and Brabham were the only factory teams at this non-championship race, Lotus with three drivers - Arundell again in the R3 spare - Brabham with only one. Predictably Clark was on pole but new, experimental driveshafts failed at the start and Brabham led Arundell home. Taylor held a good second early on but lost oil from his transaxle and consequently suffered c.w.p. failure. Ironically, following practice troubles with the Colotti six speed 'box he had switched cars with Arundell. Clark joined in towards the end of the race to set a new lap record and took over a second off his pole time, which in turn was three and a half seconds faster than his '62 pole.

**Nurburgring (D) August 4**
*German Grand Prix*
*Clark.... Q: 1/R:2*
*Taylor... Q: 18/R:8*
This weekend Taylor had a regular ZF fitted to R2. Clark again secured pole position with on this occasion only Surtees' Ferrari close to his time. Bandini's privately entered BRM was next up, ahead of Hill who practised but did not race the monocoque. Clark made the best start but his Climax 'fluffed' at Adenau bridge and Ginther and Surtees went ahead. Clark retook Ginther but later his engine lapsed onto seven cylinders, then he had to hold the car in gear. That allowed Surtees to put Ferrari back into the winner's circle while second was a worthy result for Clark in the difficult circumstances. Unhappy with this handling, and also bugged by a misfire, Taylor finished one 14 mile lap down.

• Diary continues on page 86

ease of chassis installation. It had been developed to allow installation of the FWMV ahead of the driver in a version of the short lived '61 Ferguson Research four wheel drive car which never in fact saw the light of day.

A flat plane crankshaft is simply a regular in line four engine's mirror image shaft with crank pins phased at 180 degrees. Fitted with it, a 90 degree V8 runs as two four cylinder engines sharing a common crankshaft and this allows full advantage to be taken of exhaust pressure wave tuning principles without having to combine pipes from opposite banks.

The disadvantage of a flat plane crankshaft is secondary out of balance. The out of balance forces originate from variations in the acceleration of the reciprocating components moving up from b.d.c. and those moving down from t.d.c. Acting in the plane of the cylinders, in a flat plane crankshaft 90 degree V8 engine these forces are resolved into a horizontal force which alternates direction at twice engine speed.

The secondary out of balance thus manifests itself as a side to side shake of the shaft. This vibration must be contained by the crankcase structure and can cause headaches, particularly in a gear timing drive if parts are not heavy enough to dampen it down. The FWMV was, of course, part gear, part chain driven and Hassan told the S.A.E.: 'to our surprise the vibration of the engine was not noticeably different to that fitted with a 90 degree phased crankshaft. There was a small improvement in bearing loading, and a slight reduction in weight due to the simplified system of crankshaft balance weights'.

The flat plane crankshaft was thus advantageous, particularly since it simplified the exhaust system and it became standard equipment from '63 onwards. For BRM a flat plane crankshaft allowed a properly tuned exhaust system. Another feature of Climax' '63 season was the on track development of the Lucas injection system which overcame the tendency for engines to be run with a dangerously weak mixture. This practice followed marked over-richness on acceleration caused by the FWMV's carburettor

*The '63 T car - R3 - awaits its wheels in the inclined Francorchamps pit lane. Note the simple, solid Girling brake discs stopped by two pot calipers. Equipped with long stroke carburettor engine, R3 was needed come Sunday, Taylor writing off R5 in a qualifying shunt.*

# • Diary continued

**Karlskoga (S) August 11**
*Kanonloppet*
*Clark.... Q: 2/R:1*
*Taylor... Q: 3/R:2*
*Heat 1 results:*
*Clark.... 1*
*Taylor... 2*
*Heat 2 results:*
*Clark.... 3*
*Taylor... 2*

Clark in R3 (still with Mark II engine) and Taylor in R2 defeated Brabham, his temporary teammate Denny Hulme and a host of privateers this minor two heat affair. Brabham took pole as Clark grappled with brake bothers and led the first heat until his engine cut out. Both heats were wet and the Lotus duo let Brabham through in the second heat, content to win on aggregate.

**Enna Pergusa (I) August 18**
*Mediterranean Grand Prix*
*Taylor... Q: 3/R:NR*
*Arundell. Q: 6/R:2*

Taylor and Arundell met Brabham and Surtees at Enna. Aside from Surtees, Bandini's ex-works BRM - next on the grid - proved the greatest threat to Team Lotus, Brabham in trouble early on. Taylor made the best start, then was resigned to chasing Surtees while Bandini passed Arundell and came through to challenge for second.

Bandini was playing it rough. Taylor was forced wide by the BRM, getting a wheel on the dirt. Showered by stones he lost control of R2. The car hit an earth bank, was launched into the air, then hit a steel guard rail. It was totally destroyed but had thrown out its driver at around 100m.p.h. after the first impact. Taylor somehow survived without serious injury. Arundell just pipped Bandini at the post, Surtees winning comfortably.

**Zeltweg (A) September 1**
*Austrian (non championship) Grand Prix*
*Clark.... Q: 1/R:NR*
*Arundell. Q: 3/R:DNS*

Although R2 was now extinct a new chassis had been built up at the factory, R6 and this was equipped with a flat plane crankshaft version of the Mark III Climax and a five speed Hewland gearbox for Clark to try. With Taylor convalescing Arundell backed Clark with R3 - in regular trim - while R4 stayed in the transporter, ready for Clark's use at Monza the following weekend. Brabham again provided the chief opposition. Arundell was third quickest in practice but a contractural dispute with his Formula Junior team prevented him racing. Pole man Clark fought Brabham and Ireland's BRP-BRM, then a failed oil pipe sidelined the Lotus as it was starting to draw away.

**Monza (I) September 8**
*Italian Grand Prix*
*Clark.... Q: 3/R:1*
*Spence... Q: 9/R:13-NR*

Since Monza also clashed with Arundell's schedule Mike Spence was invited to drive R6 while Clark concentrated on R4. However, Hewland troubles led to Spence racing R3 from mid grid. Meanwhile, Clark suffered a lack of r.p.m. and Surtees and Hill headed him on the grid. Surtees had a brand new semi monocoque Ferrari chassis, while Hill now had the monocoque BRM going more to his liking. Hill took the lead, followed closely by Surtees and Clark. Surtees took the lead on lap four of 86, Clark moved into second spot.

For a dozen laps Clark fought the new Ferrari, running in its slipstream, sometimes alongside. Then he saw the V6 blow. Left without a tow, Clark was caught by Hill and Gurney's Brabham. The three cars were equally matched, slipstreaming each other and Hill and Gurney took turns at leading. Hill suffered a slipping clutch then Gurney suffered a fuel feed problem leaving Clark a lap up on everyone.

The lead had changed no less than 27 times. In mid field, Spence subsequently lost the engine of R3 after a solid drive. Clark meanwhile romped home to the victory which made him undisputed World Champion and secured the Manufacturer's Cup for Lotus and Coventry Climax.

**Oulton Park (GB) September 21**
*Gold Cup*
*Clark.... Q: 1/R:1*
*Taylor... Q: 4/R:NR*

This weekend Ferrari was absent but the British teams were out in force. Hill again reverted to a spaceframe BRM and he matched Clark's practice best. Nevertheless, in his usual car Clark was once more on pole while Ginther's third best time was matched by Taylor in R6 which was running a new six speed Colotti-based transaxle. Ginther made the best start but Clark straight away made amends for that and once more was simply unbeatable. He made the first 100m.p.h. lap of the circuit on his lonely run to victory. Taylor fell into mid field and suffered c.w.p. failure.

**Watkins Glen (USA) October 6**
*US Grand Prix*
*Clark.... Q: 2/R:3*
*Taylor... Q: 7/R:NR*
*Rodriguez Q: 13/R:NR*

Here R3 - still with a Mark II engine - was entrusted to Pedro Rodriguez while Clark and Taylor had their Oulton cars. BRM did not ship out its monocoque and Hill put his regular machine on pole, just 0.1 second faster than Clark with Surtees 0.2 second further away in the semi-monocoque Ferrari but racing the older spaceframe design.

Clark suffered a rogue fuel pressure pump which caused him to flatten his battery on the grid, consequently he started well over a lap in arrears. His fuel pump continued to play up yet he carved through the field to an eventual third place, albeit one lap behind Hill who inherited victory when Surtees' engine failed. Ginther was second while Clark set fastest lap and in

• Diary continues on page 88

float chamber layout. Lotus ran only its spare car on carburettors, the injected Mark III engine was standard. During the season it relocated 'the bomb' from the gearbox to the nose, in search of the necessary cooling air.

Since there was only a small temperature differential between the back and the front of the radiator, the pump was set conveniently behind it, alongside the oil tank. However, this location brought problems in the heat of South Africa: fuel vaporisation was caused by the pump running too hot. In response it was moved ahead of the radiator. Another problem of the adaptation to fuel injection was that of the choking of the fine filters within the pump. This was caused by the handling of fuel in churns and funnels and since this practice could not be avoided it led to a more easily accessible filter being provided.

A headache for Lotus early in the season was the ZF gearbox. As we have noted, this component left Clark walking home through the streets of Monte Carlo. Its replacement played up during qualifying at Francorchamps. According to *Motor Sport*'s man Jenkinson, "assembly trouble" plagued Clark's 'boxes at this stage. It was subsequently overcome, he was later able to report. Interestingly, at the 'Ring a new ZF went into Clark's car with reverse gear left out since the reverse gear selectors were on the same shaft as the forward gear selectors and therefore could potentially cause trouble.

Earlier, when chassis R2 replaced the wrecked R5 at Zandvoort it carried the new Type 35 Colotti six speed 'box debuted at Francorchamps by the Walker team. Taylor regularly drove R2 and the Colotti 'box played up on him at Silverstone and Solitude and at the 'Ring a replacement ZF was fitted. R2 was replaced by R6 at Zeltweg and this car tried a Hewland five speed 'box as used by the Brabham team. Clark drove R6 - with the flat plane engine - at Zeltweg, then Spence took it over for Monza where troubles with the Hewland 'box saw him race R3 instead.

Mike Hewland, in fact, considered use of his VW based constant mesh, dog engagement Mark Four gearbox in Formula One "pushing it a bit". The Mark Four had really been intended as Formula Junior and Sports Car kit. Its gears ran on steel caged needle roller bearings which usefully proved relatively insensitive to lubrication.

# • Diary continued

all probability would have beaten the BRMs, but for his delay. Both Rodriguez and Taylor had fallen from the pack, suffering engine and electrical failure respectively, Rodriguez having run as high as sixth early on.

**Mexico City (MX) October 27**
*Mexican Grand Prix*
*Clark.... Q: 1/R:1*
*Taylor... Q:12/R:NR*
*Rodriguez Q:20/R:NR*
Mexico had a representative field for its first World Championship race. For Lotus there was trouble in practice: Rodriguez' engine broke its timing drive and it had to be repaired with Reynolds chain from the local bicycle shop. Clark needed a gearbox rebuild to stop his ZF jumping out of second but otherwise was untroubled on his way to pole position, then his sixth World Championship win of the year. Ferrari had two semi monocoques on the gird, Surtees lining up alongside Clark but Gurney, then Brabham led an increasingly distant pursuit. Fuel surge in the closing stages could not stop another Clark demonstration. Meanwhile, Taylor fell out of midfield with camshaft bearing failure, Rodriguez with rear suspension mount failure.

**Kyalami (ZA) December 14**
*Rand Grand Prix*
*Clark.... Q: 4/R:16*
*Taylor... Q:2/R:10*
*(Aggregate results)*
*Heat 1 results:*
*Clark.... 19*
*Taylor... 17*
*Heat 2 results:*
*Clark.... 5*
*Taylor... 6*
Lotus sent R4 plus a new chassis - R7 - for Taylor to Kyalami. Ferrari provided the only factory opposition and Surtees and Bandini finished first and second, Surtees from pole. Taylor had outqualified Bandini but the team was plagued by fuel pump overheating and consequently fuel vaporisation. Taylor finished tenth while, more greatly troubled, Clark was 16th from fourth on the grid.

**East London (ZA) December 28**
*South African Grand Prix*
*Clark.... Q: 1/R:1*
*Taylor... Q:8/R:8*
The fuel vaporisation troubles saw Lotus relocate 'the bomb' ahead of the radiator and this brought a return to form. Although suffering gear selection problems during qualifying, Clark took pole ahead of Brabham and Gurney, the grid including all the regular World Championship contenders. The semi monocoque Ferraris were next up ahead of the spaceframe BRMs and Taylor. Taylor was 1.5 seconds off pole - his strongest qualifying performance of any World Championship event this season. The Brabhams won the start but Clark was ahead by the end of the lap and went on to win convincingly. Taylor was eighth, three laps down after a bolt in the gear selection mechanism worked loose.

Like the ZF, the Hewland had a magnesium case and it ran a ZF l.s.d. However, unlike the ZF its intermediate ratios could be changed, and within 30 minutes. It could thus be geared to properly suit any circuit. There was not necessarily much in this in terms of lap time but it did mean that the car could be geared better for certain sections of certain tracks.

Five c.w.p. ratio-determined speeds were enough for Clark throughout the season. Nevertheless, six speeds were generally the order of the day in '63, only ZF and Hewland shunning six speed development. For Oulton Park R6 was fitted with another Colotti six speeder, in which the c.w.p. failed. R6 was one of two new chassis introduced in '63, R7 following for the South African finale. R7 was the last Type 25. As we have seen, four cars came forward from '62 and Taylor wrote two of these off, R5 at Francorchamps, R2 at Enna.

R6 introduced a number of chassis modifications. It featured modified pick up points for the radius rods on tub and redesigned rods plus a new flexible throttle cable and an ammeter and a pressure gauge for the Lucas pump on the instrument panel. The twin Bendix pumps had now been dispensed with, in favour of a clever surge system relying on non-return valves. The fuel now went back from the side tanks into a collector pot in the seat tank. The new throttle cable replaced the usual Bowden motorcycle-type which was prone to stick and jam in the face of engine heat and its inevitably somewhat tortuous route. It was more rigid and was of the positive push and pull type, allowing a driver to hook back the accelerator to counter a sticking throttle.

*From Pau (page 87) to East London (opposite) equipped with fuel injection, the Climax V8 - Lotus was the Formula One car of 1963.*

Chassis developments in '63 were subtle. At Spa Clark tried an experimental windscreen arrangement with, in effect, the normal perspex screen cut down and reshaped and a moulding set ahead of it so as to deflect air upwards in a jet over the top of the cockpit. The driver then sat in still air behind a curtain of high velocity air through which he could see more clearly than through a perspex screen. Of course, this clever wind deflector screen arrangement required a suitably modified cockpit/scuttle/nose section.

Clark raced Spa with a conventional screen but at Zandvoort a wind deflector modified slightly

## CHASSIS LOG

R2

For Taylor at Zandvoort, Rheims and Silverstone. For Arundell at Solitude. For Taylor at Nurburgring, Karlskoga and Enna Pergusa. Written off at Enna Pergusa.

R3

For Clark at Snetterton. For Taylor at Pau, Imola, Aintree and Silverstone. T car at Monte Carlo (lent to Brabham), Spa Francorchamps (raced by Taylor) and Zandvoort. For Arundell at Rheims. T car at Silverstone. For Taylor at Solitude. For Clark at Kalskoga. For Arundell at Enna Pergusa and Zeltweg. For Spence at Monza. For Rodriguez at Watkins Glen and Mexico City.

R4

For Clark at Monte Carlo, Spa Francorchamps, Zandvoort, Rheims, Silverstone, Solitude, Nurburgring, Monza, Oulton Park, Watkins Glen, Mexico City, Kyalami and East London.

R5

For Clark at Pau, Imola, Aintree and Silverstone. For Taylor at Monte Carlo and Spa Francorchamps. Written off at Spa Francorchamps.

R6

New for Clark at Zeltweg. T car at Monza. For Taylor at Oulton Park, Watkins Glen and Mexico City.

R7

New for Taylor at Kyalami. For Taylor at East London.

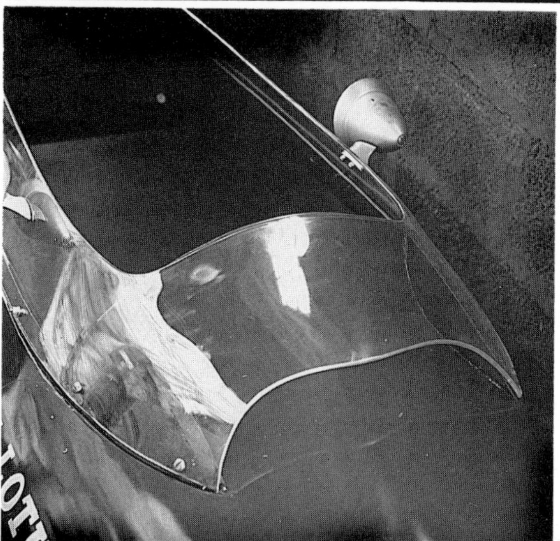

for a stronger updraught was a feature of R4. However, at Rheims Clark reverted to the old perspex screen due to the real danger of stones penetrating the air barrier. Both race cars ran an air deflector screen from Silverstone but at Monza Chapman decided to replace the air deflector with a more conventional screen on race morning. Silverstone saw the first appearance of a broad yellow stripe down the centre of the car.

At Solitude Clark tried experimental driveshafts, to his cost. All three cars at the German race had outer ends with Hardy Spicer u.j.s, as usual but each sported a different design for the spider that bolted the shaft to the rubber 'doughnut' at the inner end. R3, the test car, had the original - '62-style - shafts with fabricated sheet steel spiders. R2 had the '63 pattern with forged solid one-piece spiders while R4 had new experimental spiders formed from taper tube welded directly onto the shaft. Alas, these experimental shafts had allowed the bolt heads on the doughnut to foul the final drive housing and Clark's drive failed as he let the clutch in at the start...

At Rheims Clark tried 700 rather than 650 (section height) tyres but the car would not pull them and he reverted to the normal (28" rather than 29" overall) tyre diameter. This season tyre development by Dunlop was arguably more significant than any chassis development undertaken by Lotus. The R6 tyre was first used at Pau and testing in the wet at Silverstone with Clark after the International Trophy revealed the impressive gain of three seconds over the green spot R5. However, in the dry drivers had found the new tyre difficult to drive, making the car nervous and the breakaway point sudden and ill defined. In essence, this was due to the new carcase proving too stiff.

In response Dunlop reverted to late '62 R5-type construction from Monaco onwards. The slightly wider and thus flatter tread of the R6 helped overcome the former temperature problem and D12-type synthetic (green spot) rubber could still be run everywhere, as originally planned. The reversion to the older-style construction was something of a compromise but it made the tyre more driveable.

Highly effective the modified R6 was, too. For the first time Formula One tyres offered the potential for a co-efficient of friction higher than

*Chassis experiments i[n] '63 included a nove[l] 'wind deflector' scree[n] (upper left) and the fiv[e] speed Hewland (lowe[r] left). However, ther[e] was no standar[d] specification in '63 a[s] witness the detail o[f] chassis R3 in Austri[a] in the centre shot retaining '62-styl[e] oil tan[k]*

*n 1963 the Lotus 25 ained its distinctive ellow stripe (below). lark is pictured flat out Oulton Park and (left) hallenging Graham Hill Monza. At Monza lark clinched the 1963 rown and he celebrated home two weeks later ith a runaway Oulton ark victory.*

1.0. Certainly, the best chassis managed to defy gravity with the modified R6 and lap times fell everywhere in '63. And again the Lotus 25 arguably made the most of tyre potential, though gradually other chassis designers were starting to catch up with Chapman...

Nevertheless, given the promise of the Lotus 25 in '62 it was surprising that few other constructors had jumped on the monocoque bandwagon for '63. The Alfred Moss/Ken Gregory British Racing Partnership (BRP) came closest to a Lotus 25 copy with a very similar tub carrying Lotus wheels, hubs and uprights and a BRM V8 engine. BRP had previously run the UDT-Laystall Lotus 24-BRMs and it had produced its own monocoque in response to Chapman's refusal to productionise the Type 25.

BRM introduced a chassis that attempted to incorporate a proper monocoque centre section while from Monza Ferrari went for a stressed skin reinforced, tubular-based chassis tub. Others - notably Cooper and Brabham - stayed with conventional tube frame cars, as raced by BRM and Ferrari for much of the season. The ATS employed a spaceframe, as did the equally unsuccessful BRM-engined Scirocco.

The Cooper was a little heavy (and McLaren and Maggs failed to make much of a mark) but the Brabham was very close to the weight limit. Although it had a podgy chassis with outboard springs front and rear, the Brabham was fast in a straightline, matching Type 25 top speed with the same engine. Its Hewland gearbox might have sapped less power than the ZF. Equally, the Brabham might have been a match for the Lotus aerodynamically; neither were wind tunnel tested. However, its suspension was notably stiffer, its chassis less rigid.

It also transpired that the monocoque BRM lacked rigidity. The BRM featured a high sided central monocoque structure with tubular outriggers to carry the suspension and powertrain. A similar approach had been seen in the P25 BRM of the mid Fifties. The problem with it was that strength was lacking at the firewall bulkhead due to the cockpit opening. BRM planned a full length monocoque for '64.

Ferrari made a major chassis advance with the semi-monocoque car it introduced at Monza. Compared to its predecessors, this Maranello machine featured a lower frontal area with a heavily reclined seating position and a slimmer, stiffer fuselage. This Lotus-style attention to drag reduction and rigidity followed Surtees' arrival at Maranello.

The Monza Ferrari had Lotus-like front and rear suspension, although with inboard rear brakes. The chassis structure was notably more compact and featured Lotus-inspired torsion boxes, within which were the tubes that Ferrari refused to abandon. Innovatively, the Jano-designed chassis was designed to end altogether with the cockpit.

The intended V8 engine was to be bolted to the rear bulkhead as a fully stressed chassis member, as the Lancia V8 engine had been in Jano's mid Fifties D50. With the new mid engined Ferrari a sub frame mounted on the bellhousing carried the rear suspension. Since the V8 was not ready for use in '63, a modified 120 degree V6 was employed and this required the support of a sub frame.

The Monza V6 proved surprisingly strong. In '63 the 120 degree V6 Ferrari engine employed Bosch high pressure direct injection, this the work of Michael May. The system was adapted from that seen on the Mercedes W196 of the mid Fifties and with it the modified engine introduced at Monza gave a quoted 210b.h.p. at 11,000r.p.m.

In contrast, Chiti's V8 ATS was a flop, to the chagrin of Ferrari's '61 World Champion Phil Hill. BRM, however, made good progress. The switch to a flat crank and full exhaust tuning was a major step for Bourne, considerably improving the power band. Ferrari and BRM developments were an ominously growing threat to the domination of Lotus and Coventry Climax.

# P.S.

# Living On

At the end of the 1963 season there were four surviving Lotus 25 chassis and two of these - R3 and R7 - were sold to Reg Parnell (Racing) Ltd. Following the death of his father, Tim Parnell took over the running of the ex-Bowmaker outfit. No further 25s were produced, the new Type 33 coming on stream for 1964.

The 33 was a refined version of the World Championship winning machine with a reworked, lighter monocoque, a modified ZF gearbox (featuring a revised selector mechanism with the interlock mechanism at the gearbox) and important 'corner' changes including a switch to 13" rims. The 33 continued the Type 25 chassis numbering sequence in view of its close relationship and the prototype was thus R8. Since the 33 was not a major step from the 25 only R8 was readied for the new season, the two 25s retained updated as interim cars, chassis R6 having its corners modified to suit the new wheels and tyres.

The 13" wheel wore a tyre with a tread up from 5.2" to 7.2" in width at the rear, and this was matched by an increase in section height to 6.85" (though nominally it was a 700 tyre) so that in total it was 26.7" high. The new type R6 tyre was designed for a 9.5" rim width and had an 11.8" section width, giving it an aspect ratio of 58%,

## CHASSIS LOG

1964

R3

Sold to Reg Parnell (Racing) Ltd

R4

For Arundell at Snetterton and Goodwood. For Spence at Syracuse. For Arundell at Silverstone, Monte Carlo, Zandvoort, Spa Francorchamps and Rouen. For Spence at Brands Hatch. For Mitter at Solitude. For Spence at Enna Pergusa. Subsequently sold to Reg Parnell (Racing) Ltd.

R6

For Clark at Snetterton and Goodwood. For Arundell at Syracuse and Aintree. For Clark at Silverstone, Monte Carlo, Zandvoort, Spa Francorchamps, Rouen and Brands Hatch. For Spence at Solitude. For Mitter at Nurburgring. For Clark at Enna Pergusa. T car at Zeltweg. For Clark at Monza and Watkins Glen. For Spence at Mexico City.

R7

Sold to Reg Parnell (Racing) Ltd.

1965

R6

For Clark at Goodwood. For Rodriguez at Silverstone. T car at Spa Francorchamps. For Clark at Charade. T car at Silverstone. For Spence at Zandvoort. For Mitter at Nurburgring. For Clark at Enna Pergusa. For Russo at Monza. For Solana at Watkins Glen and Mexico.

'aving won the World
hampionship with
lark and the two year
d Lotus 25, Chapman
troduced the Type 33
1964.
'owever, some existing
5 chassis continued to
rve the works team.
Iere Clark is pictured
chassis R6 at
Ionaco in '64, exiting
e Station Hairpin.

well down on earlier tyres. Otherwise, the rear and matching 13" front was familiar having the usual construction, compound and tread pattern. Of course, the big jump in width put a significant extra amount of rubber on the track and for the first time the contact patch, while still roughly oval in shape, was wider than it was long.

That was a highly significant change and the new tyre had opened up the door to a coefficient of friction as high as 1.1. However, it was inherently more difficult to drive on the limit and demanded a smooth, neat, "on rails" driving style. More rubber put even more emphasis upon the benefits of a sophisticated suspension system with soft springing and tight control of camber. Of course, Clark already had the right driving style and the Lotus 25 had the right suspension characteristics. Rivals could no longer get away with anything less.

This season Lotus switched between 550 and 600 fronts and reverted back to 15" tyres at Spa Francorchamps since rain looked imminent. Chapman reasoned that the narrower treaded tyre would be less prone to aquaplaning while the reduced grip in the dry was to a large extent offset by the lower frontal area of the tyre, aerodynamic drag particularly important on the fast circuit. However, the 15" rears were 700s whereas lower 650s had been used throughout '63.

Aside from smaller discs, appropriately revised geometry for suspension and steering was called for to suit the 13" rims. New uprights were designed and at the rear there was a relocation of the lower radius rod chassis pick up underneath the tub. The aim was to reduce the toe-in of the rear wheels under conditions of bump or droop caused by the rod pulling the upright forward and inward. That was attempted by setting the pick up directly ahead of the inner pick up of the reversed lower wishbone, effectively producing an extremely wide based wishbone.

Clark won the Goodwood Trophy race on March 30 in R6, then debuted the 33 in the Aintree 200 on April 18. Alas, contesting the lead he tangled with backmarkers and crashed heavily, putting the unique machine out of action for the early season Grands Prix. Thus, at Monaco and Zandvoort Team Lotus fielded only R4 and R6. Unhappy with the new 13" wheels and tyres, Lotus had converted R6 back to 15" wheels for later pre-championship races.

At Monaco R4 was still on the regular 15" wheels but had the revised gearbox seen on the 33 while R6 was back to the new 13" wheels and tyres and had stronger 33-type driveshafts and a further modified rear suspension as well as the same gearbox and linkage revision. The rear suspension now followed 33 pattern with the upper radius rod relocated, above hub level and in line with the transverse link. This further helped reduce toe steer and ensured a more equitable share of tractive and braking torque between radius rod and transverse link.

In R6, Clark led Monaco until the rear anti roll bar mounting broke, then he won the Dutch Grand Prix. At Zandvoort R4 had 13" wheels and tyres, the new driveshafts and a full Type 33 steering assembly (unlike R6) and both cars had strengthend rear anti roll bar mountings. Both cars were back on 15" wheels for the Belgian Grand Prix and R6 was then back with 25-style rear suspension. Rebuilt, R8 was available again but Clark preferred R6, and he took another win.

Due to a suspect engine R6 - back on 13" wheels and tyres with 33-type rear suspension - rather than R8 was used at Rouen but a stone entered its engine inlet, breaking a valve. At Brands Hatch Clark again preferred R6 and again he won, seemingly destined for the World title double. Before the German Grand Prix he won at Solitude in R8, then for the 'Ring Team Lotus had a brace of 33s, Clark racing R9. Somehow R8 had not been the same since its rebuild, in spite of that non-championship race win. In the new R9 Clark suffered gear change trouble - a rare problem in 1964 with the modified 'box and linkage - then an engine malady and Surtees won the German Grand Prix, at last finding form in the new V8 Ferrari.

Clark finished second in R6 in the non-championship Enna race, then Bandini made it two in a row for Ferrari at Zeltweg where R6 reverted to T car status and a broken driveshaft on R9 sidelined Clark. Worried about the reliability of new style telescopic Type 33 'shafts, Clark fell back on R6 at Monza but his engine failed and Surtees took a second win. Clark stayed faithful to R6 for the United States Grand Prix but injection pump failure sidelined him. Surtees finished second to Monaco winner Graham Hill and that left the world title open to Clark, Surtees or Hill, according to the result of the Mexican finale. Clark led in a 33 until his engine failed in the late stages and second to Gurney's Brabham was good enough for Surtees to clinch the title.

Meanwhile, Arundell had been replaced by Spence following a major Formula Two race shunt and the latter finished fourth in Mexico in R6. Earlier, Arundell had been on the rostrum at Aintree in R6; in R4 at Goodwood, Syracuse (sharing with Spence), Silverstone (the International Trophy), Monaco and Zandvoort. Following the introduction of R9 Parnell had been able to acquire R4. All the Parnell cars ran in the 13" wheel and tyre specification and carried a BRM V8 engine and a Hewland gearbox.

By the end of '64 Type 33 R10 was operational and R11 came on stream early in 1965. Nevertheless, R6 continued to serve the factory in 1965 and was the chassis in which a four valve version of the Climax V8 was introduced at Goodwood on April 19. The so called Mark IV version of the FWMV run in 1964 had featured an ultra-short stroke - 72.39 x 45.47mm - and slightly enlarged - 1.37in. - exhaust valves. It had a stroke:bore ratio of 0.63 and a piston area in excess of 50 sq.in. However, it retained the traditional small bore induction tracts (designed for high air velocity) and could not breathe freely enough to exploit its radical dimensions. Revs and power were up by only 2.5%. Few Mark IV engines were produced. The model was designed to be the first step in development of the four valve per cylinder engine which Climax felt was necessary in view of the emerging twelve cylinder challenge from Ferrari and Honda.

The Mark VI four valve headed version (following a one-off two valve Mark V unit featuring slightly enlarged inlet valves) was only bench tested in '64, running late. The four valve head featured pent roof chambers and a relatively wide valve angle. Anticipated performance was extremely reluctant to emerge but advanced ignition timing was eventually found to be the key. Power then went up to 210b.h.p. running to 10,500r.p.m. with torque of 196lb.in. at 8,500r.p.m. Power was strong over a 3,500 rather than 2,500r.p.m. range. Clark won at Goodwood then went on to win at Spa Francorchamps, Silverstone, and the Nurburgring using the Mark VI unit in Type 33 chassis R11.

The four valve FWMV engine was only one part of the Climax strategy, Hassan also developing a 16 cylinder four valve engine. This was likewise conceived in '63 but the prototype was not ready for testing until late in '64. In two valve form power was disappointing and there was insufficient time for development. Thus, the planned Lotus 39 sixteen cylinder car, a spin off from the 25/33 series, never saw the light of day. By 1965 BRM, Ferrari and Honda were all joining in the four valve game, yet Clark proved a two valve V8 could still win.

After Goodwood R6 continued its life with a regular two valve engine, using the new R7 tyre introduced this season. Dunlop faced competition once more, in the form of Goodyear. Its new R7 featured a new tread compound - known as yellow spot - and a new tread pattern for improved wet grip. A tyre with the main axis of its contact patch transverse is more prone to aquaplaning, hence the renewed attention to water clearance. The last of Dunlop's convex crown racing tyres, the R7 was essentially the same size as the '64 R6 but represented a major improvement in terms of compound thanks to revised chemistry: there was a distinct difference in polymer terms, moving from an oil extended polymer to a "high styrene" polymer. The new yellow spot tyre endowed the old R6 chassis with an unprecedented level of grip.

Remarkably Clark won the French Grand Prix reverting to R6, while he won the South African and Dutch Grands Prix in a two valve 33 en route to a convincing second world title with six victories from nine races, having shown the potential to win just about anywhere. That includes Indianapolis, for after two years of disappointment Clark had at last won the 500 mile race.

A rare defeat in Formula One in '65 was once again by Siffert's private Brabham-BMW in the Enna slipstreamer. Number two driver Spence and various third string drivers also handled R6 from time to time, generally without distinction though Rodriguez finished the International Trophy race fourth. R6 was subsequently sold to Bonnier who fitted an enlarged engine with which to contest the first year of the 3.0 litre Formula.